Human Genetics and Medicine

Cyril A. Clarke

Studies in Biology no 20

Books in the Series

Other volumes in preparation

The Institute of Biology's
Studies in Biology no. 20

Human Genetics
and Medicine

WITHDRAWN

by Professor Cyril A. Clarke
C.B.E., M.D., F.R.C.P., F.R.C.O.G., F.R.S.

*Head of Department of Medicine and Director of
the Nuffield Unit of Medical Genetics,
University of Liverpool.
Consultant Physician, Liverpool United Hospitals, and
Liverpool Regional Hospital Board*

New York · St. Martin's Press

First edition 1970

First published in
the United States of America in 1970
by St. Martin's Press, Inc,
175 Fifth Avenue, New York, New York

First published in Great Britain by
Edward Arnold (Publishers) Ltd

.

Library of Congress Catalog Card Number: 76–121344

Printed in Great Britain by
William Clowes and Sons Ltd, London and Beccles

General Preface to the Series

It is no longer possible for one textbook to cover the whole field of Biology and to remain sufficiently up to date. At the same time students at school, and indeed those in their first year at universities, must be contemporary in their biological outlook and know where the most important developments are taking place.

The Biological Education Committee, set up jointly by the Royal Society and the Institute of Biology, is sponsoring, therefore, the production of a series of booklets dealing with limited biological topics in which recent progress has been most rapid and important.

A feature of the series is that the booklets indicate as clearly as possible the methods that have been employed in elucidating the problems with which they deal. Wherever appropriate there are suggestions for practical work for the student. To ensure that each booklet is kept up to date, comments and questions about the contents may be sent to the author or the Institute.

1970

INSTITUTE OF BIOLOGY
41 Queen's Gate
London, S.W.7

Preface

There is a rumour prevalent in the common rooms of the medical faculties that headmasters tend to keep medicine for their less brilliant scholars, and that the best scientific brains are advised to go into mathematics, chemistry or physics. It is the hope of the author that this book may go a little way to remedying this view, for it should be made clear to young people that medicine is a most exciting subject intellectually and that with the biological explosion upon us there are many problems in medicine on the verge of being solved and the discoveries are likely to be made by those who see their subject in relation to general biology.

Various authors and editors have kindly given me permission to reproduce figures and tables from their publications, and these are all acknowledged where they appear. If the work is not included in the list of references at the end, or in the bibliography, the full reference is given under the figure or table. I should like particularly to express my indebtedness to Mr. Per Saugman and to Messrs. Blackwell for their kindness in allowing me to include parts of my book *Genetics for the Clinician*.

Liverpool, 1970

C.A.C.

Contents

Introduction

Genetics is of increasing importance in medicine partly because more is now known about the basic facts of inheritance and partly because, with the control of many infections by antibiotics and public health measures, genetic disorders are relatively more frequent than they were.

The most obvious practical use of medical genetics is in 'counselling', that is, in advising patients of the risks of disease to themselves or their offspring if there is a genetic skeleton in the family cupboard. Of less value at present, but with great promise for the future, is that medical genetics may also help us to outwit our inheritance. Diseases do not always manifest themselves even in the presence of the appropriate genetic constitution, and it will become increasingly possible to offset the action of deleterious genes.

Nevertheless it is first necessary to understand classical Mendelian genetics in the context of disease. The corner-stone is the single gene type of pedigree in which affected and unaffected individuals segregate like Mendel's peas, but it will soon be appreciated that illness is much more often caused by a subtle interaction between genetic and environmental factors, so that it is obligatory to understand as well something of polygenic inheritance.

In the early chapters of this book therefore, the various methods of inheritance are discussed, the first being that of a typical dominant trait.

1.1   Dominant inheritance: Huntington's chorea as an example

Huntington's chorea (HC) is an inherited disease characterized by involuntary muscular movement and progressive mental deterioration. The age of onset is usually about 35 years so that the majority of those affected can produce a family before they are aware of their plight. The disease is transmitted by an autosomal dominant gene (see Fig. 1–1), so both sexes are equally affected and, moreover, because penetrance (see glossary) is complete the disorder never skips a generation. It is rare (one estimate in this country is five cases per 100,000 of the population) and so affected individuals are always heterozygotes (see below for explanation of this point). Very unfortunately there is no test, either biochemical or electrical, which can tell us who in a family will develop the disease and so far linkage studies with a genetic marker (as for example that between the nail-patella syndrome and the ABO blood group locus, see chapter 6) have been unhelpful.

The disease, introduced into North America by two Suffolk immigrants in 1630, derives its name from the U.S. doctor who first described it in 1872. Fraser Roberts writes "the boy George Huntington, driving through a wooded lane in Long Island while accompanying his father on professional rounds, 'suddenly came upon two women, mother and daughter, both tall, thin, almost cadaverous; both bowing, twisting, grimacing,' so that he 'stared in wonderment, almost in fear'. The memory was as vivid more than fifty years later, long after he had translated into fact the youthful resolve, born that day, to make chorea the subject of his first contribution to medical science: a resolve which led him into many a home where

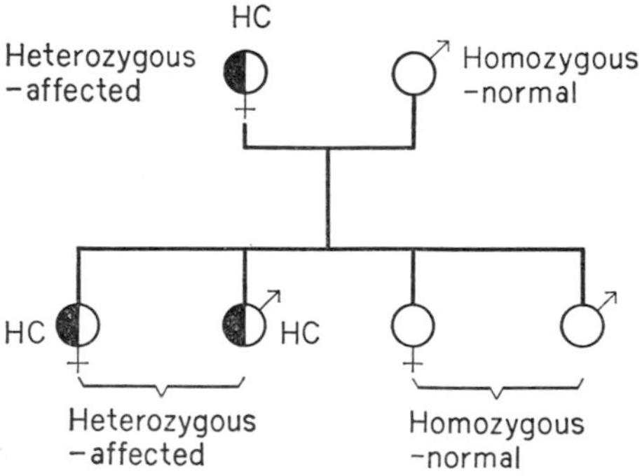

Fig. 1–1   Pedigree of Huntington's chorea (HC). (By courtesy of Messrs Blackwell.)

The following symbols are used synonymously in the illustrations of this book
  □ or ♂ for male
  ○ or ♀ for female

HC

Heterozygous –affected   Homozygous –normal

HC   HC

Heterozygous –affected   Homozygous –normal

the bearers of the gene waited with stern Calvinistic stoicism for the dreadful fate that Providence had meted out to them".

Huntington's chorea arises in the first instance because of a mutation at the HC locus which is on one of the autosomes (which one is not known). Subsequent affected individuals will almost invariably be heterozygous for the condition because they will marry normal partners. Though theoretically an affected × affected mating *could* take place and produce a homozygote, this would probably be lethal, and the gene is so rare that it is most unlikely to occur. Where a trait is common, such as the various ABO blood types, it is readily possible to have the homozygote, e.g. blood group OO or AA.

1.2 The problem of controls in assessing a mutation rate

A matter of considerable interest is the reason for the persistence of the disease. 'Recurrent mutation' is the obvious answer, but another explanation is that, since heightened sexual desire (increased libido) is one of the early symptoms, affected individuals will have more children than their unaffected siblings (brothers and sisters) and this in fact has been found to be so. The mutation rate, therefore, could be extremely low (or even nonexistent) since, on the assumption that unaffected sibs behave as normal individuals, the biological fitness is higher than unity (see glossary). However, to use the unaffected sibs may not be the right comparison because, since they are aware of the inheritable nature of the disease, they may marry late or limit their families. In fact where the fitness of HC individuals is compared with *normal* people it is well below unity (0·81) and if these are the right controls (as seems likely) then a higher mutation rate must be invoked. It might be thought that this is only of theoretical importance but in an age of radiation hazards *any* information about mutation rates is of great importance, and HC shows how difficult it is to assess it—a value for biological fitness being necessary for the calculation.

The situation in HC should be compared with that of duodenal ulcer (see page 40) and it will be clear that it is perfectly legitimate to draw opposite conclusions about the best type of control in the two diseases.

1.3 Recessive inheritance: fibrocystic disease as an example

Fibrocystic disease (FCD) is a generalized disorder of mucus secreting glands, particularly those in the pancreas, the intestines and the lungs. The mucus is more viscid than normal and, as a result, dried up secretions block the glands and their ducts so that they atrophy and become replaced by scar tissue. However, the cells in the pancreas which secrete insulin are not affected so diabetes does not occur. Another feature is that the sweat contains a higher concentration of sodium chloride than normal.

The disease is fairly common, occurring once in about 2000 births, and it accounts for between 1 per cent and 2 per cent of admissions to children's hospitals. The outlook for a sufferer is not good even with antibiotics and pancreatic extracts, many of the children dying of pneumonia, though a few survive to adult life.

The disease is controlled by an autosomal recessive gene so that both sexes are equally affected and as a rule neither parent manifests the condition. Figure 1–2 shows that one in four individuals on average will be affected in a sibship where the disease is occurring.

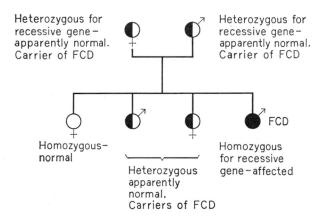

Fig. 1–2 Mating between two individuals heterozygous for the gene controlling FCD. Pedigree of fibrocystic disease (FCD). (By courtesy of Messrs Blackwell.)

1.3.1 *Possible explanations of the high frequency of fibrocystic disease*

The fact that the disease is often met with makes the genetics of considerable interest and any of the following would explain the frequency:

(a) A high mutation rate—but this would have to be so high as, *a priori*, to be unlikely.

(b) Several different genes, each with its own mutation rate, might cause the condition which could vary in severity according to which of several alleles was responsible. In other words, the disease might be heterogeneous (as is often the case with other conditions).

(c) The heterozygotes, i.e. those individuals which carry one dose of the gene and which form 5 per cent of the entire population (see page 30 for the way in which this figure is calculated), might have an advantage, that is be biologically fitter, than the normal homozygotes—in other words the disease might constitute a polymorphic system (see page

21). What this advantage of the heterozygotes may be or may have been is unknown, though PENROSE (1959) thinks that they 'at one time or in one climate, in famine or in pestilence, were at a huge advantage, but that the genes are now on their way out, moving too slowly to be noticeable'. This may or may not be correct but with improvements in technique (see below) it will soon be possible to identify the heterozygotes with certainty and then their fitness could be tested directly by their reproductive performance, i.e. how many children they had.

1.4 Detection of heterozygotes in fibrocystic disease of the pancreas

(a) It was at one time thought that the sodium content of the sweat in the heterozygotes might be helpful in identification. It is true that on average these have a somewhat higher value than do normal people yet the range is very great and there is much overlap. Furthermore, allowance is often not made for age. The sodium content of the sweat rises as one gets older and therefore comparison must be made between patients of similar age groups. Figure 1–3 demonstrates this point, where it will be seen that there is practically no difference in the sodium content of the sweat between parents of affected individuals, i.e. known heterozygotes, and that of normal controls *of the same age group*.

(b) A much more promising way of detecting the heterozygotes (carriers) is by a special staining technique using certain skin cells grown in culture. These are the fibroblasts and DANES and BEARN (1968) have shown that in children with fibrocystic disease they have a peculiar staining property, called metachromasia, this meaning that the tissues stain a different colour from that of the dye employed. The same research workers next looked at the parents of children with fibrocystic disease. These, of course, were necessarily heterozygotes and in all instances a similar cytoplasmic metachromasia was seen, and in one family the metachromasia was detected also in 2 of the 4 grandparents. On the other hand, cultures derived from 26 unrelated normal individuals and from 11 patients with miscellaneous diseases showed only an occasional metachromatic cell. Figure 1–4 shows a pedigree illustrating heterozygotes detected by this method, which is likely to prove a most valuable tool, since not only could it be used for genetic advice, but also to test the hypothesis that carriers are more fertile than controls. It might also reveal heterogeneity in the disease since particular forms could show the metachromasia and others not. Some authors, even before this new technique was discovered, had investigated the family size of parents of children with cystic fibrosis (C.F.), and they *did* find when investigating 144 grandparental couples, matching three different control couples with each grandparental pair, that there was a tendency for the grandparents of C.F.

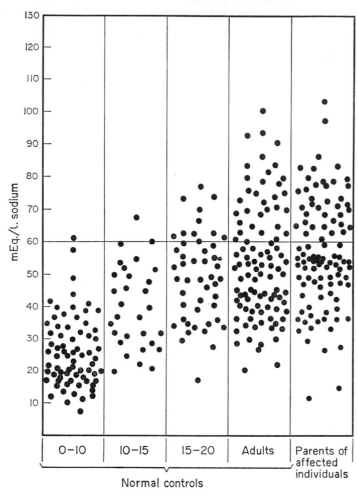

Fig. 1–3 Sodium content of sweat in relation to age. (By courtesy of Drs Anderson and Freeman and the editor of Archives of Diseases in Childhood.)

children to have larger families, though in only one of the comparisons was the difference statistically significant. The authors of the paper (DANKS *et al.*, 1965) put forward their results with great reservation, since the magnitude of the heterozygous advantage apparently shown is very much greater than would be needed to maintain the gene at a steady frequency in the community.

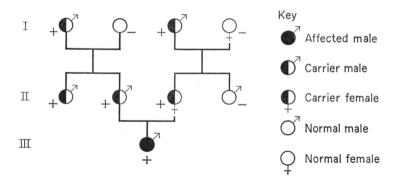

Key
● Affected male
◐ Carrier male
◑ Carrier female
○ Normal male
○ Normal female

Fig. 1–4 Pedigree of cystic fibrosis of the pancreas, a recessive condition. The + and − signs adjacent to the male and female symbols indicate whether the skin fibroblasts in cell culture showed the peculiar staining property called metachromasia. This is present in children with fibrocystic disease. Adapted from DANES and BEARN 1968, by courtesy of the authors and of the editor of the *Lancet*.

1.5 Example of a technique of mapping a chromosome

A baby with fibrocystic disease of the pancreas was found also to have the condition known as the cri du chat syndrome. This is characterized by mental deficiency and a curious mewing cry due to weakness and under-development of the upper part of the larynx, and is caused by a deletion (see glossary) of the short arm of chromosome No. 5. The parents of this child were investigated and it was found by another special immunological test (the Spock test, see glossary) that her mother, but not her father, was a carrier of fibrocystic disease (both would be expected to be). This child, therefore, had fibrocystic disease, even though she could not have been a homozygote (because of the negative test in the father). The inference is that it was because of the deletion that she had not received the dominant normal allele from her father, and consequently it was suggested that the gene controlling fibrocystic disease of the pancreas might also be on the missing short arm of chromosome 5. Other studies have not confirmed this finding. The inference rests on the reliability of the particular test for heterozygosity for fibrocystic disease of the pancreas, and more work is necessary since the test is not entirely reliable. However, this investigation is a good example of the type of situation which needs exploiting to find out whether a gene for a disease is on a particular chromosome.

Sex (X)-Linked Inheritance 2

2.1 Haemophilia as an example of sex-linked recessive inheritance

Haemophilia is an anomaly of blood coagulation (clotting) inherited as a sex-linked recessive, and is the disease which created such havoc in the royal families of Europe when introduced into them by the daughters and descendants of Queen Victoria (see Fig. 2–1). Haemorrhage, usually follow-

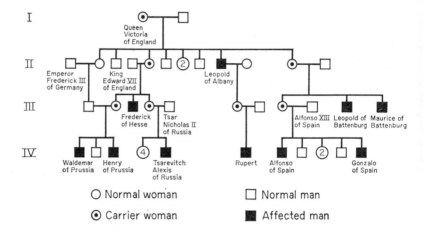

Fig. 2–1 Sex-linked recessive inheritance. Pedigree of haemophilia in the royal families of Europe. All affected individuals trace ancestry to Queen Victoria of England, who undoubtedly was a carrier. Her father was normal, nothing suggests that her mother was a carrier, and therefore Queen Victoria seems to have received a *new* mutant allele from one of her parents. It will be realized that many individuals in later generations are not included—among them our own royal family, who are quite free, being descended from an unaffected male. All Queen Victoria's children are entered in the pedigree. (By courtesy of Professor Curt Stern and Messrs Freeman.)

ing injury but sometimes spontaneous, is the essential symptom. The bleeding is of the nature of a persistent, slow oozing which is out of all proportion to the extent of the injury; this can last for weeks and may lead to profound anaemia. Cases also often present as orthopaedic problems due to recurrent haemarthroses (bleeding into the joints). The disease usually appears in early childhood or even in infancy, and it is due to the deficiency of one of the clotting factors of the blood (factor VIII, anti-haemophiliac globulin, or AHG). The severity of the condition is very variable, yet within a given family it remains constant and there may be a number of alleles of the haemophilia gene. As well as this, there is a group of conditions clinically indistinguishable from this type of haemophilia ('haemophilia A'), but which are due to a deficiency of other blood clotting factors. The best known of these, Christmas disease (or 'haemophilia B') which was called after the patient in whom it was first described, is also a sex-linked recessive, and is due to deficiency of the Christmas factor (factor IX), which is distinct from AHG. A mixture of two equal parts of blood, one from a patient with haemophilia A and the other from a patient with Christmas disease clots normally, whereas separate samples show delayed clotting. Another rather similar bleeding disease, where the level of AHG is diminished, is von Willebrand's disease, and this is inherited as an autosomal dominant. It will be mentioned later in another connection (page 11).

It must be remembered that haemophiliacs may develop entirely unrelated diseases, and the writer has seen a fatal case of intestinal haemorrhage which was thought to be due to the haemophilia but was in fact secondary to a duodenal ulcer. In this connection, it is important to realize that haemophiliacs stand operations quite well if they are suitably prepared with blood or (fresh) AHG beforehand.

The gene controlling haemophilia is situated on the X chromosome, and this is almost always what is meant by 'sex linkage' since Y linkage has very rarely been reported in Man, and several claims to its occurrence have not been substantiated on further investigation. It will be realized that since a woman is XX and a man is XY, an X-linked gene can be passed to either sex, whereas one on the Y could only go from father to son. (When a gene can only *express* itself in one sex it is said to be sex-limited or sex-controlled. This situation is described in 2·5, and is quite different from sex-linkage.) Most, though not all, sex-linked genes in Man are recessive. Just as with the autosomes, crossing over can take place between one X and the other, but crossing over between X and Y has only very rarely been reported, since there is a part of the X chromosome which does not pair with the Y.

It will readily be understood that since haemophilia is controlled by a sex-linked recessive gene, female carriers of the gene will never be affected unless they are homozygotes. This is because females have two X chromosomes and the normal gene on their second X will prevent the haemophilia gene from expressing itself—they will however pass on equal numbers of normal and abnormal X chromosomes to their offspring of both sexes, so that the offspring of carrier females will consist of half normal and half affected sons and of half normal and half carrier daughters. Owing to the rarity of the gene, females are most unlikely to be homozygotes and hence haemophiliacs, but cases have been reported and some patients have survived childbirth and borne haemophiliac sons. Males, on the other hand, will always have the disease if they possess the gene, and all their daughters will be carriers (since they can only pass on an affected X). All their sons, however, will be completely free from the disease as they will receive only a Y from their affected father. This should be apparent but it is surprising how many people with quite advanced medical knowledge do not appreciate this fact. I often ask candidates in medical examinations what proportion of a haemophiliac's sons will develop the disease provided he marries a normal woman. Nearly all candidates pause, look very wise and then say 'about 50 per cent, sir'! It must be remembered that the *men* in these affected families can always know what their children will be. Normal men will have all normal children by normal wives (and they will never develop the disease later in life as it always manifests itself early), whereas haemophiliac men, if they live long enough to have any children at all, will have all normal sons and all carrier daughters. It is those women who have, say, a haemophiliac brother, and who may have inherited the gene from a carrier mother who are in doubt, and it is sad that they cannot know for certain whether they are carriers or not, though about 85 per cent of these heterozygote carriers can probably be detected by biochemical tests.

2.2 Point mutation

In genetic counselling, which often has to be based on information from small families, it may be impossible to be sure that one is not dealing with a new mutation.

We discuss elsewhere (p. 46) chromosome changes visible under the microscope, but changes too small to be observed can occur and these are known as point mutations. FRASER ROBERTS (1970) puts the matter well: Very rarely, once in a hundred thousand or once in a million, or ten million, times a gene is not handed on in the usual way unchanged from generation to generation but undergoes a physico-chemical change, and thereafter the new gene, which is as stable as the original one, is transmitted in just the same manner. Naturally the new gene occupies the same locus on the same chromosome as the old one, and so the new and the old genes are allelomorphic. A mutation can, apparently, occur in any cell, though preferentially, or perhaps always, in cells that are dividing. If it occurs in a somatic cell (*somatic mutation*) only the descendants of that cell are affected, and there will be no transmission of the abnormality to further generations. A blue segment in the brown iris of an eye is an example of a somatic mutation.

Only mutations occurring in the germinal tract can be transmitted to offspring. These, as a fact of observation, are nearly always single events: that is, when a new dominant mutation occurs it is found in only one of the children of the parents in whom it took place. Very occasionally, however, it is found that more than one child in the sibship is affected. This is because the mutation must have occurred further back in the ancestry of the gametes. The person in whom it occurred is then a *gonadic mosaic*, part of the testis or ovary containing the cells bearing the mutant gene while the other parts contain only the unmutated gene (FRASER ROBERTS, (1970)).

It will be realized that since the chromosomes are composed of deoxyribonucleic acid (DNA) and since the order of the bases in this material determines the structure of the amino acids and hence the proteins, a change in one base of the DNA could result in the formation of a new gene.

In the case of haemophilia, there may be only a vague history of bleeding in relatives of a patient, and there may be no maternal uncles, affected or otherwise. Clearly, if the propositus (see glossary) carries a mutant gene which arose at some time prior to his conception, then his sisters are very unlikely to be carriers, and this situation must always be considered if a male comes for treatment of any X-linked recessive disorder having no family history. A *female* who was affected because mutation had occurred in a similar way would be more rarely met with, as in her case a mutation would have had to take place in both her parents. Where dominant inheritance is concerned incomplete penetrance (see glossary) causes some difficulty since a generation can be skipped completely and there is no family history in either of the parents. Another confusing factor is that genes can have variable 'expressivity' (meaning that they manifest with varying degrees of severity) and this can sometimes result in the parents passing on the gene although they were so mildly affected that they were considered normal.

2.3 A possible suppressor gene in haemophilia

There is another point which should be mentioned. The nucleus of every cell in the body (other than the germ cells) contains *all* the genes, but it is evident that in any given cell only a proportion of these are in operation, i.e. those operative in that particular part of the body. It has been demonstrated in bacteria that there are 'regulator' and 'operator' genes which combine to switch on and off the main structural genes as required, and this is thought to occur also in higher organisms, including Man. There are also abnormal inhibiting or suppressor genes which can prevent a normal gene, even though present, from exerting its effect.

We mentioned above von Willebrand's disease. Here the anti-haemophiliac factor VIII (AHG) is formed, but in a reduced concentration. Since von Willebrand's disease is an autosomal dominant, it has been suggested that perhaps the 'haemophilia gene' on the X chromosome is a suppressor gene, and that this suppresses the action of the gene controlling AHG which is on an autosome. In von Willebrand's disease, on the other hand, there is no abnormal suppressor on the X but the gene controlling factor VIII on the autosome is abnormal.

2.4   The mapping of the X chromosome

Crossing-over will be described in chapter 4 and also in chapter 6, and so will the method of calculating the cross-over value (p. 36) which indicates how far apart the genes are likely to be on the chromosome. Quite a number of genes are known to be situated on the X chromosome (some concerned with disease but many not), the best known among them being those controlling colour vision, two types of muscular dystrophy, the skin disease of ichthyosis, the two forms of haemophilia already mentioned, G6PD deficiency (see page 55) and the very important Xg blood group system. The last two conditions are detectable in the heterozygote, and the frequency of the Xg heterozygote in the European female population (i.e. the frequency of women having the gene controlling the Xg^a blood group antigen on one X chromosome but not on the other) is as high as 46 per cent. Many families, therefore, which segregate for one of the rare sex-linked conditions mentioned above will also segregate for Xg, and one does not have to search for families segregating for two rare traits. It thus becomes possible to find the relationship of the rare mutant gene to the Xg locus, and thence to one another. The distances are measured in crossover units, or map units, one map unit being equal to one per cent of crossing over. Thus if five per cent of the offspring of informative matings (see page 36) are of the 'recombinant' type—that is, they are the result of crossing over—then the two gene loci are said to be about 5 map units apart. Work is in constant progress so that the map is often altered, but EMERY (1968) gives a simple diagram of some of the loci (Fig. 2–2).

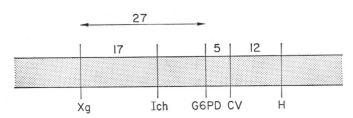

Fig. 2–2   A map of part of the human X chromosome. Distances are measured in map units and the loci are indicated as Xg = Xg blood group; Ich = Ichthyosis vulgaris; G6PD = glucose-6-phosphate dehydrogenase; CV = colour vision; H = haemophilia. (By courtesy of Prof. Emery and Messrs Livingstone.)

2.5   Sex limitation or sex control

It was mentioned earlier that genes are said to be sex-controlled or sex-limited when they can express themselves only in one sex, and this is quite different from sex-linkage. An instance is only described here for comparison. Frontal baldness only shows itself in males except on the rare occassions where a female receives the gene in double dose. The fact that an affected male can transmit the condition to his son shows that the gene responsible cannot be on his X chromosome, and the fact that he can transmit it to his daughter shows that it cannot be on the Y. Thus the gene is on an autosome but can only express itself in the male gene-complex—why this is so is unknown.

3.1 General considerations

This type of inheritance is, as the name implies, not dependent on one single gene (or pair of alleles) for which the individual is homozygous or heterozygous. It is not even dependent on genes only, but on the environment as well, and it means what it says, i.e. that many factors are at work. The genes responsible will all be genes of varying but small effect, and with varying dominance, and it is not always easy to sort out which are the inherited components responsible for the condition and which the environmental ones. The term 'polygenic' is nearly synonymous with 'multifactorial' but differs in that it only refers to the genetic component of a character controlled by many genes.

It is easy to understand that characters which are controlled by many genes show continuous variation, whereas those which are controlled by single ones show clear-cut, either/or differences. It is quite simple to visualize the fact that many genes control human height—people are not 'tall' or 'short', they vary through all degrees of tallness and shortness with a few very tall and few very short people at the two extremes. The vast majority of adults will fall in an intermediate group and if you draw a graph of their height you will obtain a 'normal curve'. There will be a sex difference and there will be racial differences, of course, and there will be the effect of nutrition, but the genes responsible for height are additive (as are those for intelligence). What is not nearly so easy, and gives rise to a great deal of very complicated mathematics, is the fact that diseases are very often multifactorially controlled. After all one either has or has not a disease—it is all very well to say that many genes add up to give you diabetes or a duodenal ulcer, but what constitutes the difference between 'disease' and 'no disease'? Here we come to the fact that there is a threshold beyond which the disease manifests itself—if you have enough genes predisposing to the disease, and also the environmental factors favour its expression, then you will have the disease. Here too there are sex differences, some diseases being more prevalent in one sex than in the other, and CARTER (1962) has done some very interesting work in this connection. He has shown that in pyloric stenosis (see pp. 66–67), which is commoner in boys than in girls, when a *girl* (i.e. the wrong sex) has the disease she has more affected relatives than does a boy with the disease. The female baby is evidently normally more resistant to the disease than the male baby, and when she does develop it this is because she has a very high concentration of predisposing genes, and this is why more of her relatives will also have this high concentration of genes and show the disease. This seems rather complicated but it serves very clearly to illustrate the threshold effect seen in multifactorial inheritance.

The study of quantitative variation is of course statistical and the mathematics that are involved are not for the amateur, but FRASER ROBERTS (1963) gives a very simple introduction to the principles, which are based on the resemblance between relatives. For each step farther away in relationship, the number of genes in common with one's relatives is halved. A parent passes on to a child half his or her chromosomes; they have half their genes in common. Clearly, the child will pass on half the genes derived from that particular parent, so a grandparent and a grandchild will have a quarter of their genes in common, and so on. With a rare* dominant autosomal gene, it will be clear on a little consideration that half the children of a person in whom it appears will receive it, a quarter of his grandchildren and an eighth of his great-grandchildren. Half the parents and sibs of an affected person are therefore like the patient and half are unlike, and the likelihood of the other types of relative being affected can be calculated in a similar way. With multifactorial inheritance, however, many genes are combining together to produce the end result. On the *average*, half of the genes are making the sib or parent just like the subject, while half of them are making them no more like him than would be an unrelated subject. The difference is that instead of half the sibs or parents being totally like, and half totally unlike, all the parents and all the sibs are tending to be half-like. All the uncles and aunts are tending to be one-quarter-like; all the cousins one-eighth-like. These measures of resemblance are termed *regressions*, and multifactorial inheritance would follow the pattern indicated if there were no dominance and all the genes were intermediate in effect. This, of course, they are not, so dominance and recessiveness have to be considered and this involves complications. One effect of dominance in multifactorial inheritance, however, remains the same even though there are variations in dominance from gene pair to gene pair, and differences in the amount of effect produced by different genes: *the reduction of the regression for sibs is always half the reduction for parents* (meaning, as will be realized, that sibs are more like the subject than are parents).

The matter is a complicated one, but the above remarks will give the reader an idea of the arguments involved. The section on high blood pressure which follows describes some of the investigations which are carried out when it is desired to determine whether a condition is multifactorially inherited or controlled by a single gene.

---

* If it were not rare, it might come in from both sides of the family and the model would not apply.

3.2 The controversy over the method of inheritance of high blood pressure (essential hypertension)

The arterial blood pressure consists of two components, the systolic, associated with the beat of the ventricles of the heart, and the diastolic, which is the constant pressure in the arteries between beats. The upper limit of normal in adults is about 140 mmHg for the systolic and 90 mmHg for the diastolic. Occasionally a definite cause, e.g. kidney disease, can be found to explain the hypertension but usually this is not the case and the condition is then said to be 'essential' or cryptogenic. Where this is so the patient often feels perfectly well, the finding being brought to light during some routine medical examination such as for life insurance. However, a family history of hypertension is often found in people with this condition and there is general agreement that inherited factors play a part in its causation. The controversy, however, has been *how* it is inherited, particularly whether as a graded character like height or as a specific 'either/or' disease entity. Some of the evidence which has been brought forward by both sides will now be discussed. The arguments are also relevant to the part played by inheritance in several other common diseases.

(a) Family studies

In 1954 HAMILTON and his colleagues investigated the frequency distribution of blood pressure at different ages and concluded that there was no natural division between the normal and the abnormal. They also surveyed the first degree relatives (fathers, mothers or children) of patients with hypertension and found no indication of a bimodal distribution such as would be expected if the population contained two groups, one hypertensive and the other not.

PLATT (1959) however felt that this unimodal distribution in the relatives might for various reasons be masking two groups. He thought it would be of interest to plot the blood pressures of relatives of propositi (people through whom the investigation of the disease had been begun) in a middle-aged group, which is when essential hypertension occurs. By concentrating on this age he largely excluded patients with hypertension due to other diseases.

He therefore took 252 siblings who were all between the ages of 45 and 60, and who were the sibs of propositi also aged from 45 to 60. He plotted the systolic and diastolic pressures of these sibs *only* (leaving out the propositi, all of whom were hypertensive) and found that the blood pressures *did* fall into two groups, even allowing for some inaccuracies of measurement. Figure 3–1 shows the distribution curves of the systolic pressure of these siblings.

This situation would be consistent with the control of essential hypertension by a single dominant gene, and this is what PLATT believes often to be the case.

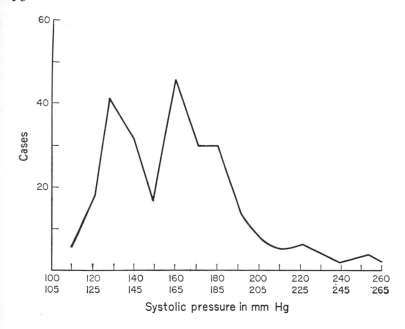

Fig. 3–1 Systolic pressures of 252 siblings aged 45–60 of hypertensives aged 45–60, showing a bimodal distribution curve. The lower row of figures represents a correction to avoid recording blood pressure in even tens. PLATT (1959), from data of HAMILTON *et al.* (1954), and SØBYE (1948). Similar findings are also found with the diastolic pressure. (By courtesy of the authors and the editor of the *Lancet*.)

(b) Population surveys

On the other hand, in 1955 and 1958 MIALL and OLDHAM had carried out two large population surveys. They showed that there was a relationship between the arterial pressure of propositi and their close relatives of the same degree at all ages no matter what the blood pressure of the propositus was. This degree (the regression of the blood pressure of relatives on that of propositi) was about 0·2. This means that the relatives of a man with a systolic blood pressure 25 mmHg higher than the mean for his age, for example, would have a pressure averaging 5 mmHg above the mean for their ages. Table 1 gives some of the actual figures which MIALL and OLDHAM found and Fig. 3–2 shows the data represented graphically, the legend explaining in detail how the regression lines have been constructed. The consistency of the regressions and the normal distribution curve (an example of which is shown in Fig. 3–3) in this large-scale investigation provide obvious support for the hypothesis of multifactorial (see p. 14) control.

Table 1   Part of a population sample (propositi and first degree relatives) taken from a Welsh survey (MIALL and OLDHAM, 1958). The mean arterial pressures are given in 5-year age groups

Age	Females								Males							
	Population sample (propositi)			First degree relatives			Population sample (propositi)			First degree relatives		
	No.	Sys-tolic	Dias-tolic	No.	Sys-tolic	Dias-tolic	No.	Sys-tolic	Dias-tolic	No.	Sys-tolic	Dias-tolic
5–	11	106·6	70·2	52	105·3	69·0	12	105·4	72·1	38	105·3	68·4
10–	10	112·0	72·5	47	112·5	71·8	9	110·8	73·6	40	114·6	73·3
15–	10	125·0	80·5	42	119·2	73·8	18	128·6	78·3	33	120·8	75·2
20–	10	122·5	75·0	43	121·2	74·8	6	126·7	78·3	37	129·5	80·9
25–	2	112·5	62·5	41	123·5	77·2	17	128·4	82·5	29	123·4	78·5
30–	13	121·4	74·8	52	126·3	80·5	12	131·3	84·6	45	129·3	84·2
35–	14	130·7	82·9	46	129·9	82·6	11	130·2	85·2	47	125·9	81·4
40–	5	134·5	86·5	47	130·3	82·6	6	128·3	85·0	33	126·6	82·7
45–	5	148·5	88·5	38	137·6	84·9	9	134·2	83·1	40	127·9	80·8
50–	8	149·4	88·8	30	148·8	87·8	7	137·5	86·1	32	141·6	89·4
55–	8	169·4	98·8	30	160·8	89·5	8	150·0	88·8	18	148·1	89·7
60–	8	180·0	93·1	19	170·1	93·8	8	146·9	87·5	25	144·1	84·7
65–	4	190·0	97·5	17	169·9	91·9	6	157·5	88·3	18	167·8	92·8
70–	3	200·8	102·5	10	173·0	91·0	3	154·2	94·2	7	148·9	85·4
75–80	2	210·0	105·0	7	212·5	103·9	2	162·5	90·0	11	154·3	78·4

Adapted from Miall and Oldham, 1958, by kind permission of the authors and the Editor of *Clinical Science*.

PICKERING (1959), summing up the evidence, felt that the multifactorial hypothesis was more satisfying than that based on a single dominant gene. He pointed out that arterial pressure, like height, was the result of a large number of variables, the elasticity of the vessels, the radii of different parts of the vascular system and the action of the heart all playing a part. PLATT (1959), on the other hand, argued that only one of the many variables may be disturbed in any particular group of hypertensives, and gives as an example the condition of aldosteronism, which is a specific endocrine upset causing hypertension, the successful treatment of which takes the patient out of the hypertensive group.

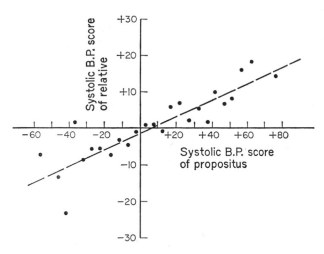

Fig. 3–2   Systolic blood pressure scores of propositi and the mean systolic scores of first degree relatives. The scores represent the deviations of blood pressure from the mean, higher pressures than the mean having positive scores and lower pressures negative ones. Each dot represents a pair of measurements. It will be seen that propositi who, for example, are + about 80 on the mean have first degree relatives whose mean pressures are about +17. The scores have been adjusted to take age and sex into consideration. The regression for the diastolic blood pressure was similar. (Miall and Oldham 1958, by courtesy of the authors and the editor of *Clinical Science*.)

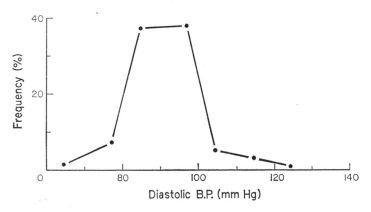

Fig. 3–3   Frequency distribution curve for 84 sibs aged 45–59 derived from propositi aged 45–59 with diastolic pressures of 100 mmHg or above. Adapted from OLDHAM *et al.* (1960). *Lancet* i, 1085–93. (By courtesy of the authors and the editor of the *Lancet*.)

(c) Twin studies

The final paper of interest is that of PLATT who in 1963 investigated the blood pressure in monozygotic identical twins, and in three pairs where the propositus had severe hypertension so had the co-twin, the measurements being:

Propositus	Twin
260/150	210/130
230/130	205/130
200/130	210/130

This concordance argues in favour of inheritance rather than environment, but it obviously does not tell you whether the method of inheritance is multifactorial or single gene. On the other hand, PLATT's data with regard to dizygous non-identical twins, where one of the twins or a non-twin sib had hypertension, suggests a single gene situation—hypertensive or normal. We are impressed with the twin studies, though the numbers are small, but remain unconvinced by his view that essential hypertension is always a unifactorial inherited disorder of middle age.

It may well be that the conflicting views of PICKERING and PLATT are not irreconcilable. After all, height is controlled multifactorially and may be secondarily affected by superimposed genetic or environmental factors, for example, various forms of dwarfism on the one hand and malnutrition on the other. Whatever be the truth of the matter a good argument often teaches one more than the straightforward 'establishment' version of a disorder, and medical conferences have been enlivened by speakers 'bickering with PICKERING or having a bat at PLATT.'

Genetic Polymorphism

4.1 Definition and general considerations

There are many polymorphic systems known in Man but at present only a few such as sickling (see 47a) and G6PD deficiency (see p. 25 and p. 55) have clinical interest. Nevertheless polymorphism is an important subject, likely to become more so in medicine, and is one of the fundamental principles of genetics. The theory is therefore discussed in some detail and much of what is written is drawn from E. B. FORD's monograph (FORD, 1965).

Genetic polymorphism is a type of variation in which individuals with clearly distinct qualities exist together in a freely interbreeding single population. FORD (1940) defined the condition as 'the occurrence together in the same habitat of two or more discontinuous forms or 'phases' of a species in such proportions that the rarest of them cannot be maintained merely by recurrent mutation'. This definition excludes several familiar types of variation. For example, the Caucasian, Mongolian and Negroid races of Man do not constitute a polymorphism since when interbreeding occurs the hybrid populations are intermediate and variable. Again, continuous variation, as in human height or blood pressure, is not an example of polymorphism. In these examples many genes are at work and the variation is brought about by the cumulative effects of segregation taking place at many loci, and not by 'switch' genes giving rise to distinct alternative forms. Seasonal forms, too, are excluded from the definition. For instance, in the Map butterfly, *Araschnia levana*, temperature or length of daylight can produce very distinct spring and summer forms but in this type of situation all members of a generation are alike and this does not constitute a polymorphic system. In addition, segregation in human populations into normals and phenylketonurics or normals and achondroplasics does not fall within the definition since these diseases are constantly being eliminated by selection and are maintained only by recurrent mutation.

The polymorphic type of discontinuous variation which we are discussing is nearly always genetic, and in a polymorphic system a continuous range of intermediates is absent. There must therefore be some very accurate switch mechanism controlled either by alleles at a single locus (such as those determining the ABO blood groups) or by the corresponding members of a super-gene (see below) which produces either one form or another.

4.2   The establishment and maintenance of polymorphism

How then does a polymorphism arise, and how is it maintained? It arises initially by mutation, and the selective effect of a mutant must be either disadvantageous (which it usually is), neutral or advantageous. In the first case the mutant will never be anything but rare as it will consistently be selected against. It has been shown first by calculation (FISHER, 1930) and later by work on *Drosophila melanogaster*, that genes always appear to have multiple effects. Except for the common lethals and semi-lethals all the mutants studied in this fly affect viability—the genes responsible for very trivial visible effects such as eye-colour, slight differences in wing venation and bristle number also alter length of life, capacity to survive under unfavourable conditions, male fertility or egg-laying propensity. Fisher calculated that the balance of a mutant and its normal allele would have to be extraordinarily exact for the two to be neutral in effect with respect to one another, so that this situation must be extremely rare. Furthermore, in the exceptional event of a mutant being 'neutral' its spread would be exceedingly slow. It follows, therefore, that where a polymorphism exists the third situation must have been operative, and the mutant gene compared with the other alleles must, under certain circumstances, have been at an advantage. If, however, the advantages were complete in every respect, the mutant gene would simply be on the way to replacing the original one and the polymorphic situation observed would be a temporary phenomenon ('transient' polymorphism). The polymorphisms with which we are concerned in this chapter are so far as is known not transient. They are 'balanced' or 'stable' polymorphisms, arising (in a manner described later) because for some reason discontinuous diversity is advantageous.

4.3   The formation of a super-gene

Particularly relevant to the establishment of polymorphisms is the formation of super-genes and this will be discussed in relation to certain forms of mimicry in butterflies, where the details have been clarified and can be readily understood. Here, within a single species, there are various forms of female each of which obtains a selective advantage by resembling another species which is distasteful to predators, such as birds. A polymorphism therefore arises and this remains balanced because an excess of mimics resembling one distasteful model would result in the predators beginning to associate that particular wing pattern with edibility, and not with inedibility. However, the mimetic wing pattern is complicated, and experiments have shown that although the 'gene' controlling it behaves as a single unit it is in fact composed of separate genes which have come to lie close together from different parts of the same chromosome or even from non-homologous chromosomes. Occasionally crossing-over occurs, breaking up the advantageous combination of the super-gene so that unusual patterns may be seen which will in general be selected against since the mimicry will then be less good.

A similar situation may have arisen in Man in the Rh blood groups. Here, there appear to be three loci controlling the antigens C or c, D or d and E or e. The corresponding antibodies are anti-C, anti-c, anti-D, anti-d (so far hypothetical), anti-E and anti-e. The commonest Rh combinations on one chromosome are CDe, cde and CDE, and it is postulated that the rarest ones (e.g. CdE) have arisen as the result of crossing over. However, the matter is much more complicated than this, for there are in fact about 20 Rh antigens and antibodies and there are probably very many mutational sites at the various loci. Furthermore there has been shown to be a 'combined' antigen depending on whether c and e are on the same chromosome or on the homologous one. Testing for this antigen has demonstrated that the c and e genes are in the same cistron (a microbiologist's word which approximates to the term super-gene). The cistron is the portion of the chromosome in which the loci are integrated for one function. The argument that c and e are in the same cistron is as follows. When genes are on the same chromosome (that is, inherited from the same parent) they are said to be in *cis*, and when the c and e genes are in *cis* they produce ce antigen (formerly called f). The c and e genes are therefore *non-complementary*—they cannot combine to form the product when they are on different chromosomes though they can when they are on the same one. According to current definition, this means that they are in the same cistron. If they *could* combine when in *trans* to form ce, they would be complementary and this would mean that they were in different cistrons.

Though it seems reasonable to regard the Rh system as forming a supergene, why it has come about is unknown, but the CDE combinations may have varying selective advantages in different genetic constitutions and it is known that the antigens have widely differing antigenicities.

4.4   Transplantation antigens—possible linkages and interactions

Of great topical interest is the suggestion that most of the genes connected with transplantation antigens in man also appear to be part of a single complex reminiscent of the Rhesus blood group system. Genes responsible for certain leucocyte antigens (which are concerned with compatibility between donor and recipient) are known from family studies to be closely linked and alleles at three of these loci have been shown to control transplantation antigens. There is evidence that the type of interaction observed between the Rh genes *c* and *e* (4.3) also takes place between two of the leucocyte antigens, and it is likely that others too are determined not simply by a single gene but by the interaction of two or more loci (see HARRIS, R., in *Selected Topics in Medical Genetics*, 1969).

4.5 Chromosomal inversions giving rise to chromosomal polymorphism

Another example of the way in which a collection of genes can operate as a unit is when there is a chromosomal inversion giving rise to chromosomal polymorphism. It has been demonstrated in *Drosophila pseudo-obscura* and *D. persimilis* that chromosome polymorphism can be maintained by heterozygous advantage (heterosis). Numerous instances have been found in wild populations in which the numbers of inversion heterozygotes exceed expectation, assuming equal viability for all three genotypes. An entirely independent proof of heterosis is provided by the fact that when a population of larvae carrying the inversions is reared in the laboratory under optimal conditions, the three genotypes in the adults have the normal proportions expected from the Hardy-Weinberg law (see page 31). When, however, the larvae are in competition for a restricted food supply it is found that the proportion of heterozygotes exceeds expectation among the adults to which they give rise.

In some cases the polymorphism consists in the number of chromosomes. For example in *Nicandra physaloides*, distantly related to the tobacco plant, the fertilized eggs with one chromosome fewer than normal are subject to delayed germination and the variation so produced is of advantage in contending with environmental fluctuations.

4.6 Heterozygous advantage and the evolution of dominance

The usual way in which polymorphisms are maintained is through the selective advantage of the heterozygotes over both homozygotes—this will keep the alternative alleles in the population. This heterozygous advantage can arise in two ways. First, as FORD (1965) very clearly explains, any gene which begins to be favoured must exist almost entirely in the heterozygous state in the initial stages of its increase since there is little chance of matings between the rare heterozygotes. If the mutant gene has a slight advantage, recessive lethals or semi-lethals which are carried on the same chromosome can be sheltered from elimination by their proximity to the advantageous mutant, *as long as they are in a heterozygous individual*. As the newly successful super-gene increases in frequency, homozygotes appear and will be handicapped by these harmful recessives (now homozygous and consequently active). Secondly, major genes always appear to have multiple effects and if one of the features for which a mutant is responsible gives it an advantage and others do not, selection will tend to make the beneficial effect dominant and the harmful ones recessive (SHEPPARD, 1953). In these circumstances the homozygotes will have both advantages *and* disadvantages since they will be homozygous for the deleterious recessive genes as well as for the successful mutant, while the heterozygotes will bear the advantageous dominant allele but only one dose of the disadvantageous recessive ones.

(The terms 'recessive' and 'dominant' should strictly never be used of genes, only of the characters they determine, since a single gene can have many effects and the same gene will often control both recessive and dominant characters.)

4.7 Some polymorphic systems in Man

A number of polymorphic systems are mentioned in other chapters of this book but here are described in more detail a few of particular interest. A comprehensive account is that of PRICE (1967).

(a) The sickle-cell trait

In spite of the large number of polymorphic systems which have been described in Man, the selective factors involved are known in only very few. The classical example is that of sickle-cell and normal haemoglobin, the genes controlling which are situated on one of the autosomes. That controlling the formation of haemoglobin S produces the sickle-cell *trait* when accompanied by the normal allele and sickle-cell *anaemia* when in double dose. The Hb^S gene has a frequency exceeding 20 per cent in several East African populations and this means that about 4 per cent of new-born children are homozygous Hb^S/Hb^S and almost all of these will die in infancy. The reason for the high frequency of Hb^S is that the heterozygotes have a considerable advantage over normal people (Hb^A/Hb^A) because when young they are more resistant to infection by malignant tertian malaria (ALLISON, 1954) and they obviously have an advantage over those who are Hb^S/Hb^S.

(b) Glucose-6-Phosphate dehydrogenase (G6PD) deficiency (see page 55)

A similar resistance to malignant tertian malaria is afforded to those carrying the X-linked gene controlling G6PD deficiency. This at first sight appears to be a wholly undesirable trait since the metabolism of glucose is abnormal, yet in some populations the incidence is as high as 10 per cent. The protection against malaria overrides the disadvantages to which G6PD-deficient individuals are liable, namely, haemolytic anaemia induced by primaquine and other drugs; certain types of jaundice, occurring in infants (chiefly in Mediterranean races); and the liability in Caucasians of a proportion of G6PD-deficient individuals to develop jaundice after taking aspirin. This matter is dealt with in more detail in Chapter 9 and the theoretical aspects of a polymorphism controlled by an X-linked gene are discussed in chapter 5 (5.3).

(c) The ABO blood group polymorphism

The known world distribution of the blood group frequencies is strong evidence for the action of natural selection on some at least of the blood group systems. Although the relative frequencies of the phenotypes A, B and O vary markedly over very short distances, some of the other systems show much more gradual change with distance. This may be in part due to lack of detailed knowledge, but there is no doubt that there is a real contrast in the degree of geographical variation between the ABO groups and some of the other systems. Therefore, as E. B. FORD suggested, it is well worth while looking at diseases to see if a particular ABO blood group predisposes (even though very slightly) to particular disorders.

4.8 Differential susceptibility to infectious diseases

One good reason for particular attention being paid to some infectious diseases is the fact that several micro-organisms are known to possess antigens very similar to human blood substances. The thesis is that the world distribution of the ABO blood groups may have been influenced by the history of the great pandemics of infectious diseases of former times, particularly those with a high mortality such as plague and smallpox. The most interesting studies have been carried out in relation to smallpox, as in this case there is the opportunity to study the problem in those parts of Asia where smallpox is highly endemic today. It was predicted that smallpox should show a more severe course and a higher mortality in those individuals of blood groups A and AB than in those of groups B and O. The argument was based on experimental evidence that the vaccinia virus, and by inference the variola (smallpox) virus, possessed an antigen similar to blood group A substance. Thus, blood group B and O individuals who possess a natural anti-A antibody might be expected to be more likely to neutralize the virus during the viraemic stage and so sustain a milder course of disease. The hypothesis received adverse criticism and evidence was produced that the A-like antigen demonstrated was present *in the egg material on which the vaccinia virus was grown and not present in the virus*.

The experimental basis for the thesis in relation to smallpox is thus in considerable doubt. However, the epidemiological evidence is of great interest. It has been found that reactions to vaccination and, in particular, encephalitis (inflammation of the brain) were more common in people with the blood group A gene than in those without. Several studies of the natural history of smallpox in patients of different ABO blood groups have been made with conflicting results. A recent survey was designed to test the hypothesis under more critical conditions and to avoid some of the faults of previous studies. The research workers aimed at the complete ascertainment of cases of smallpox occurring over a certain period in selected highly endemic areas of West Bengal and Bihar (India). The survey was confined to rural areas where few people had been previously vaccinated and where little modern medical treatment was available. The choice of a control population for such a study is always a matter of some complexity. In populations as mixed as the ones studied there is always the

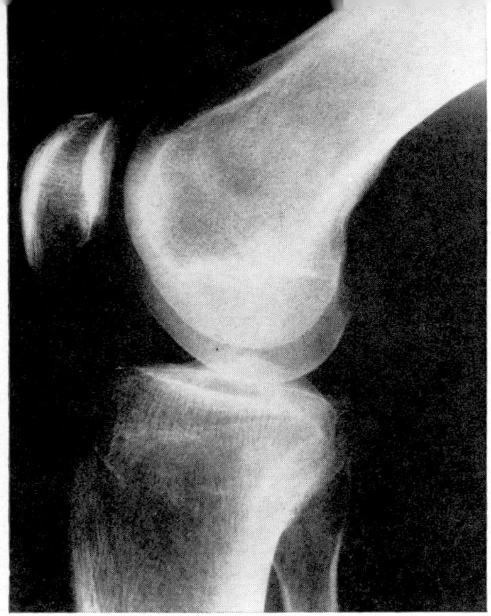

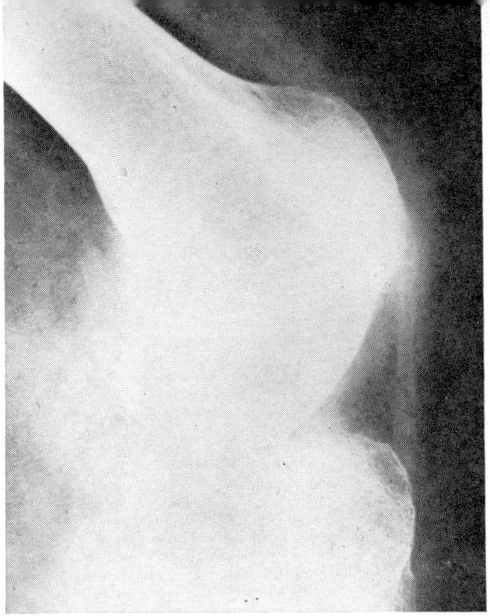

Plate 1 (*far left*) Normal patella (knee cap).

Plate 2 (*left*) Absent patella.

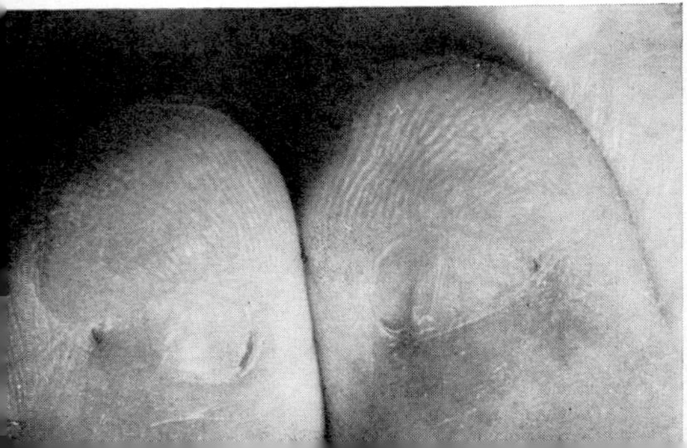

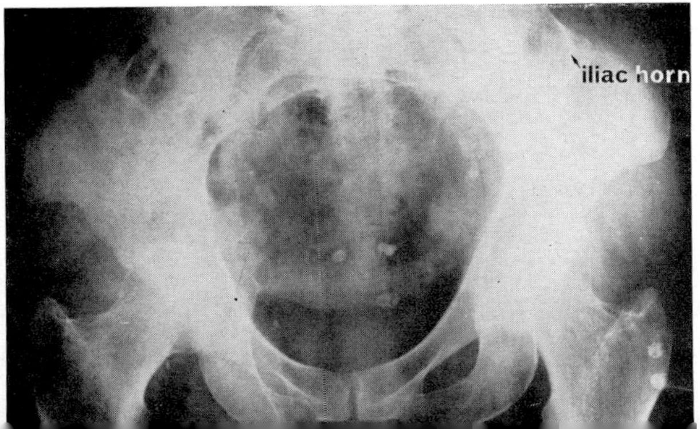

Plate 3 (*far left*) Dystrophy (abnormal growth) of finger nails.

Plate 4 (*left*) Iliac horns on pelvis.

Iliac horn

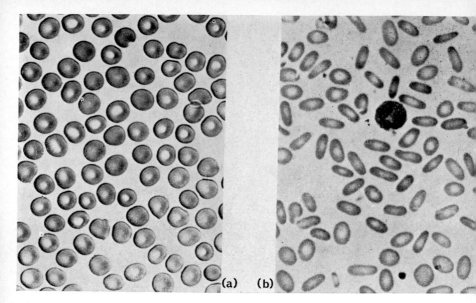

Plate 5 (a) Normal red blood cells (×600); (b) Elliptocytotic red blood cells (×600). (By courtesy of Dr. C. O. Carter and Penguin Books Ltd.)

Plate 6 Barium meal X-ray showing: A. Normal duodenal cap (the first part of the duodenum). B. Pyloric canal. C. Lesser curvature of stomach. (By courtesy of Dr. G. Scarrow)

Plate 7 A. Grossly deformed (because of scarring) duodenal cap. B. Barium filling an ulcer crater in the duodenum. C. Beginning of jejunum. D. Lesser curvature of stomach. E. Peristaltic wave. (By courtesy of Dr. G. Scarrow)

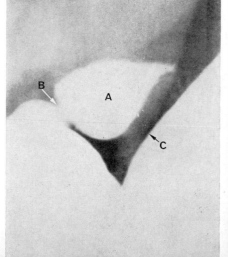

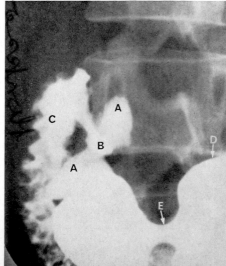

possibility that one section of the population was inbred for a long period, leading to a different distribution of ABO genes from that of the rest of the population, and that this section might for *other* reasons have a greater or lesser susceptibility to smallpox. In this way an apparent association between blood group and susceptibility might be found (stratification effect). To avoid this the severely exposed but unaffected siblings were used as controls.

It was shown that individuals of blood groups A or AB *were* much more liable to develop smallpox than those of groups B and O and, moreover, the course of the disease tended to be more severe in the former. The mortality was significantly higher in individuals possessing the blood group A gene than in those without (VOGEL and CHAKRAVARTTI, 1966).

This work therefore should stimulate renewed attempts to find an immunological or other basis for the relationship.

4.9   Differential susceptibility to chronic 'adult' diseases

As is discussed in Chapter 7 duodenal ulcer is commoner in people who are group O than in those of the other ABO groups. Cancer of the stomach is more frequently found in individuals who are group A and a similar finding is also reported in pernicious anaemia, a disease in which there is no acid secretion in the stomach (as is often the case, too, in stomach cancer). However the effect of these diseases on the frequencies of the A, B and O genes is certainly very small since the mortality from them chiefly occurs after the reproductive period is over—but this may not always have been so.

4.10   The maintenance of the Rh blood group polymorphism

Here we have a most puzzling problem. Why, when the most important mechanism for keeping a polymorphism in existence appears to be the advantage of the heterozygote, do we find in the Rh situation that there is strong selection against the heterozygote? Any foetus born of an Rh negative mother, if it be Rh positive, must be heterozygous and is in danger of suffering from Rhesus haemolytic disease (see page 60) and though this is by no means invariable, the fact that the loss is always in the heterozygote constitutes a serious difficulty in explaining the polymorphism. Even if the homozygotes were equally advantageous, the fact that for every child that dies there is destruction of one D and one d gene would mean that whichever of the two alleles was rarer to begin with would eventually be eliminated.

Several explanations have been put forward to explain why this has not taken place. The first is that parents who have lost a child will 'compensate' to replace it, and end up by having more children than those parents who had lost none. However, this cannot be the whole explanation because it has been shown mathematically that compensation will not lead to a polymorphism which is stable. Thus below a certain critical gene frequency, the value of which depends on the compensation effect, Rh negatives will still tend to decrease in frequency but above it they will tend completely to replace Rh positives in the population. Consequently we need some other selective effect to account for the persistence of the polymorphism. There is the possibility that in very primitive populations a reduction in the number of children owing to deaths from haemolytic disease would leave more food for the rest, thereby increasing the mean number of children reaching maturity in small families above that in large families, under famine conditions. This has been known to occur in birds, where the parents were unable to feed large clutches adequately. However, it seems a very speculative explanation in Man.

Another suggestion is that the polymorphism may have occurred in the first place by the d gene establishing itself and increasing owing to genetic drift (see glossary) and being thereafter selected for—why we do not know—until there were two races, one high in D and one high in d. Race mixture after that would account for the high d frequency in Western Europe, support for this being that there are even now high d races—among the Basques and the Berbers. Several originally high d races have also been thought to be a possibility, but if this were the case it is surprising that there is not more variation in the frequency of the gene in different areas.

5.1 The explanation of the Hardy-Weinberg law

This is a theoretical chapter which is concerned with the Hardy-Weinberg law, and it is not an over-statement to say that when a student of medicine really grasps the principles underlying it he has made a very great step towards understanding genetics. The law demonstrates:

(a) That with certain provisos, if there are two or more contrasting alleles in a population their proportions will remain the same (i.e. in equilibrium) from generation to generation, and

(b) that, even if one of the alleles is extremely rare, there are still a surprisingly large number of heterozygotes in the population.

The strict provisos are that neither allele is being selected for or against (but the formula is useful even when a certain amount of selection is known to be present), and that random mating is taking place—that is, any individual has an equal chance of mating with any other individual with regard to the trait in question. This will be most nearly reached when we are dealing with a character such as a blood group. It clearly does not apply when we consider a factor such as intelligence, where there is a tendency for like to marry like (assortative mating).

Let us see how the formula works out, for example, with the genes controlling blue and brown eye colour, it being assumed, for the sake of the demonstration, that there are only these two alternative alleles and that brown eye colour is dominant to blue. We are concerned with the frequencies with which the two genes occur. Let these be p for the allele controlling brown eye colour and q for that controlling blue eye colour. When p and q are expressed as fractions of the total the gene frequencies of the alternative alleles in a population must add up to 1, and therefore $p+q=1$.

It will be seen that there are three possible genotypes—BB (homozygous brown), bb (homozygous blue) and Bb (heterozygous), any one of which is equally likely to mate with any other.

Bearing in mind that the two alleles segregate in the formation of germ cells and come together in random order in fertilization, we can calculate the proportions of the three genotypes (and therefore find out how many of the brown-eyed people are homozygotes and how many heterozygotes) provided we know the frequency in the population of one of the homozygotes.

In this case we are able to do so because the character is recognizable and people with blue eyes are assumed to be homozygous for the recessive allele. The Hardy-Weinberg formula is as follows:

$$1 = p^2 + 2pq + q^2 = (p+q)(p+q)$$

1 = the whole population with which we are concerned
p^2 = the frequency of one homozygote (i.e. individuals, *not* alleles)
$2pq$ = the frequency of heterozygotes (individuals)
q^2 = the frequency of the other homozygote (individuals)

Let us now substitute some actual numbers and see how the proportions of the three phenotypes work out. Suppose that 64 per cent of the population are blue-eyed. Since we know by the study of pedigrees that these are the homozygous recessives, we start our calculations with this value, calling it 0·64, and this is q^2. q therefore = 0·8 and $p = 1 - 0·8 = 0·2$. These are the frequencies of the *alleles*. The frequency of the individuals homozygous for p can now be found, i.e. p^2, which is 0·04 = 4 per cent. We can also calculate $2pq$, which is 0·32 and 32 per cent of the population are therefore heterozygotes. It will be seen that:

$$p^2 + 2pq + q^2 = 0·04 + 0·32 + 0·64 = 1$$

It will be appreciated that in this calculation the confusing factor is the switching from frequencies of genotypes (individuals) to gene frequencies and then back again. We just have to realize that p^2, $2pq$ and q^2 refer to the proportions of individuals in a population and that is what really matters because among them may be our patients.

Since we may not always know which allele is recessive it may be necessary to study many pedigrees, or in the case of animals to carry out breeding experiments, in order to obtain this information.

The example of eye-colour given above is a very simple one (and we realize over-simplified from the point of view of its inheritance). In fact the figures with which we are presented are often much less manageable. For instance, let us consider a condition such as fibrocystic disease of the pancreas, which has an incidence in the population of about 1 in 2,000. We know that as it is inherited as a recessive, 1 person in 2,000 is homozygous for the gene. q^2 therefore is 1/2,000 and q, the frequency of the recessive gene, is about 1/44 or 0·0224. p, the frequency of the normal gene, is $1 - q$, that is 0·9776.

$$2pq = 2 \times 0·0224 \times 0·9776 = 0·0438 \quad \text{i.e. about 1 in 23}$$

that is, as many as 5 per cent of the population will be heterozygous for the gene, and given random mating and no selection the frequency of heterozygotes will remain at 5 per cent from generation to generation. The Hardy-Weinberg formula can be demonstrated to be true by working out and counting all the possible offspring of all the possible matings between the three genotypes (see, for example, CLARKE 1964).

5.2 Calculation of the Hardy-Weinberg equilibrium on a small number of individuals

We sometimes want to work out the gene frequencies, or the frequency of the heterozygotes, when we have a limited number of observed cases to work on. Suppose, for instance, we had 71 individuals and we knew (or assumed) that five of these were homozygous for a recessive gene. To find the gene frequency here we should take the number of recessives (5) and divide it by the total number of individuals (71) which is 0·0704. We should then take the square root of this, which is about 0·27, and this would be the gene frequency of the recessive allele. The gene frequency of the dominant allele would therefore be 0·73 and the proportion of heterozygotes could be worked out as already shown.

5.3 The Hardy-Weinberg law and X-linkage

An interesting situation is found where genes are sex-linked on the X chromosome. In the female there are the usual three possible genotypes and their frequencies will be as before, $p^2 : 2pq : q^2$. However, in the male there is no heterozygote and the genotype frequency is $p : q$. The gene frequency can be arrived at simply by counting the proportion of affected to unaffected males. Having arrived at this figure the frequency of the female carriers can be estimated very accurately.

5.4 Gene frequencies

If we consider the ABO blood groups, the most obvious way of recording their distribution is by their phenotypic frequencies, i.e. the proportions of people who type as A, B, AB or O. We have seen how to calculate the frequencies of the heterozygotes among those who are phenotypically the same as the homozygous dominants, and it might be thought that this was enough for our needs. However, geneticists tend to think more and more in terms of gene rather than of phenotype frequencies. This is partly because genes are more fundamental and partly because the situation becomes less complex—for example, in the ABO blood groups there are only three gene frequencies but four phenotypes, and in the Rhesus blood group system there are very many phenotypes—or rather in this case chromosomal constitutions (because in the Rhesus system there is not just one set of alleles). So we too must try to learn to think in terms of gene frequencies—though in practice we are bound to calculate these in the operation of the Hardy-Weinberg law, before we can find out the proportions of the heterozygote and the dominant homozygote. If in any given case we are calculating this, and we find that the observed proportions of the three phenotypes differ significantly from the expected which we have calculated, we may be sure either that random mating is not taking place or that one of the alleles is being selected for at the expense of the other and the population is not in genetic equilibrium. However, the fit between observed and expected is tolerably good even if the requirements of the law are not strictly fulfilled.

The main importance of the Hardy-Weinberg law to the student is that it brings home to him the fact that carriers of a deleterious trait are very much more frequent than one might expect from the frequency of those individuals who actually have the disease. Table 2 gives some examples.

Table 2

Disorder controlled by recessive gene	Frequency of affected (q^2)	Frequency of carriers $(2pq)$
Diabetes mellitus (some doubt about method of inheritance; it is uncertain whether in fact the disease is always determined by a recessive gene)	About 1 in 200 (0·005)	1 in 7·7 (0·132)
Albinism	About 1 in 20,000 (0·00005)	1 in 71·9 (0·0139)
Phenylketonuria (see page 66)	About 1 in 25,000 (0·00004)	1 in 80 (0·0125)
Amaurotic family idiocy (a lethal condition associated with blindness)	About 1 in 40,000 (0·000025)	1 in 100·5 (0·00995)
Alkaptonuria (a rare inborn error of metabolism associated with darkening of the urine on standing)	About 1 in 1,000,000 (0·000001)	1 in 502·5 (0·00199)

(Adapted from Clarke (1964) by courtesy of Messrs Blackwell.)

Genetic Linkage 6

6.1 General

In this chapter the principle is dealt with before the diseases, the latter often being relatively harmless and not of much medical significance. Genes are said to be linked when they, or more accurately the loci (positions) which they occupy, are situated on the same chromosome. The reason for saying 'locus' rather than 'gene' is that at any given locus the gene may be one or other of a series of allelomorphs (see glossary), e.g. either the blood group gene controlling (or responsible for) A, *or* B *or* O.

Superficially it might be thought that since all the genes on a chromosome are inherited together, linked characters would be readily appreciated by looking at a pedigree, but it is clear on a little thought that the matter is not as simple as this. First of all, it is impossible to detect linkage unless two characters are segregating in a family. For example, no information could be obtained regarding linkage of, say, eye-colour and the ABO blood groups (to give an entirely hypothetical example) from a family segregating for blue and brown eyes but in which all the individuals were group O. When the matter of different allelomorphs (such as the ABO blood groups) is in question it will also be realized that a certain character may be linked with one of these allelomorphs, O for instance, in one family and with A in another. Crossing-over (see glossary) must also always be thought of, because occasionally genes will change places and two characters which are linked in several members of a family may become separated in other members because crossing-over has taken place.

It may come as a surprise to learn that the firmly established autosomal (see glossary) linkages in man are very few, whereas sex-linkage (see glossary) is quite common but a different problem and it is dealt with under haemophilia (p. 8). Much the best way to understand linkage is to study actual pedigrees and two proved autosomal linkages will now be discussed in some detail.

6.2 The nail-patella syndrome and the ABO blood group locus
(linkage discovered by RENWICK and LAWLER in 1955)

A syndrome is a group of abnormalities which constitutes a recognizable disease, and in the nail-patella syndrome there are malformations of the skeletal system consisting of absent or hypoplastic (underdeveloped) patellae (knee caps), dystrophy (abnormal growth) of some or all of the finger nails, abnormalities of the elbow joints and frequently the presence of iliac horns (small projections from the flat bones of the pelvis), these being usually demonstrable only on X-ray. Plates 1 to 4 show some of these features. The condition is an ideal one for studying linkage for the following reasons: (*a*) It is inherited as an autosomal dominant and has never been known to skip a generation—it is therefore always detectable when present, provided the family is big enough: (*b*) it carries little disability and does not shorten life and there are therefore often large families and several generations to study: (*c*) the striking nature of the condition means that family reports are usually accurate. It will quickly be realized that the other character studied, the ABO blood group, is also ideal, as everybody is either O, A, B or AB. However, to detect linkage the right type of family must be observed, this being the offspring of a double back-cross.

6.2.1.   *Example of a double back-cross mating*

A double back-cross is a mating between one person who is heterozygous for the two characters under discussion and another who is homozygous for them. For example, such a mating would be that of a woman who was blood group A, but carrying O, and heterozygous for the nail-patella syndrome (the gene is so rare that she would not be a homozygote—this has never been reported) and a man who was skeletally normal and homozygous for group O (i.e. OO). Such a situation is shown in Fig. 6–1, where the nail-patella syndrome has been inherited with blood group A.

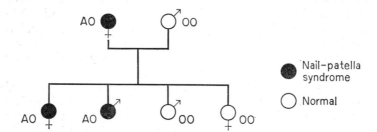

Fig. 6–1   Example of double back-cross mating. (By courtesy of Messrs Blackwell.)

It must be noted (i) that it is not possible to type the genotype AO, but it can be inferred from family studies, e.g. any person who types as A and has an O parent must be AO. (ii) that a much bigger pedigree than that shown would be necessary to *prove* the linkage.

6.2.2   *Linkage masked by dominance*

In the next pedigree (Fig. 6–2) part of a family is shown in order to demonstrate one of the elementary complexities of linkage studies. At first sight there might not appear to be linkage at all as in generation I the nail-patella syndrome appears in an A individual (I.1), in the next in two O

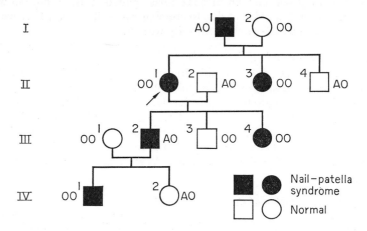

Fig. 6–2 Example of linkage masked by dominance. (By courtesy of Messrs Blackwell.)

people (II.1, the proposita, indicated by an arrow, and II.3), in the next in an A and an O (III.2 and 4), and in the next in an O (IV.1). In fact, however, the linkage is only masked by the dominance of group A. The proposita (II.1) has received the nail-patella gene with her group O, and she has handed them on together to her son, III.2. As, however, the mother of III.2 was group O he must have received O from her and A from his father. He types as an A individual because A is dominant to O and the linkage of the syndrome with O is masked by this dominance of A. In

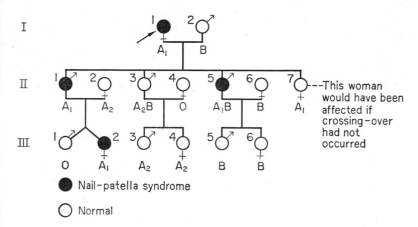

Fig. 6–3 Crossing-over in a nail-patella family. (By courtesy of Messrs Blackwell.)

generation IV it will be seen that III.2 has handed on the condition with O again. The situation is not due to crossing-over—if it were, IV.1 would have received the nail-patella deformity with A.

6.2.3   Crossing-over in linkage studies

Another pedigree (Fig. 6–3), this time of a Liverpool family, shows what happens when crossing-over does take place. Here the nail-patella syndrome is linked with group A_1, as in I.1, II.1, II.5 and III.2. Crossing-over has occurred at gamete formation in I.1, after the birth of II.5 and before the birth of II.7, who is, as will be seen, blood group A_1 and yet is *not* affected. It will be noticed that the other A individuals in this family who are unaffected are A_2 and not A_1. (A_1 and A_2 are alleles and are distinguishable.)

6.2.4   The calculation of the cross-over value

The cross-over value, about 12 per cent, in Fig. 6–3 agrees with that found in many families by Renwick and Lawler. It is calculated by looking at those individuals where the linkage can be assessed, i.e. II.1, II.3, II.5, II.7, III.1, III.2, III.5 and III.6. In one case out of the 8 (12 per cent) where the linkage could be detected a *new* combination is seen instead of the previous one, and this is quite close linkage. If the cross-over value reaches 50 per cent it will be clear that there is an equal likelihood of the characters occurring separately as there is of them occurring together, and therefore there is no linkage at all, but 'free recombination'.

6.2.5   Comparison of cross-over values in women and in men

It is of great interest that RENWICK (1963)* analysed the linkage data from 27 pedigrees of the nail-patella syndrome and found that crossing-over in respect of the nail-patella and ABO loci takes place twice as often in women as in men, and that in men it takes place less frequently as they grow older. This is the first investigation of its kind in Man, and is in accord with what happens at certain, but not all, loci in the mouse (in *Drosophila* it is well known that no crossing-over occurs in males.) The implication of Renwick's sex difference findings might have to be considered in the mapping of chromosomes (see p. 7 and p. 12).

6.3   Elliptocytosis (ovalocytosis) and the Rh blood group system

Elliptocytosis is an abnormality of the red blood cells inherited as an autosomal dominant, the majority of the cells appearing elliptical, like Rugby footballs, instead of spherical (see Plate 5). The condition is usually harmless though one form of it can give rise to anaemia, even in the heterozygote. LAWLER and SANDLER (1954) found that the gene responsible for

---

* See also Renwick, J. H. and Schultze, J., (1965) *Ann. Num. Genet.* **28**, 379–92.

elliptocytosis was linked to those controlling the Rhesus (Rh) blood group system, and it was later discovered that this linked gene was the harmless one, the other form of elliptocytosis (causing anaemia) *not* being linked to Rh. This knowledge is very useful clinically, since members of a family carrying the linked form can be told that their abnormality will cause no harm. Conversely, if someone is carrying the unlinked form they should be advised not to marry their first cousin in which case they might produce offspring more severely affected than themselves (the gene is so rare that they are most unlikely to marry a heterozygote in the general population).

The Rh blood group system seems extremely complicated but all that need be grasped here is that it consists of three pairs of allelomorphs, CDE/cde. These are so closely linked on the chromosome that they behave as one gene, but it will be realized that they can occur in many different combinations (see also p. 23).

In Fig. 6–4 it will be seen that elliptocytosis is linked to the genotype

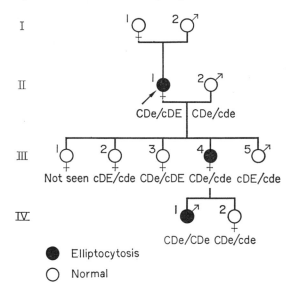

Fig. 6–4   Elliptocytosis and the Rh blood group system. (By courtesy of Messrs Blackwell.)

CDe. The propositus, II.1 is CDe/cDE, and she marries a man who is CDe/cde and therefore there is an 'affected' CDe chromosome and *also* an 'unaffected' one. Now it will be clear that any of the offspring who inherit cde must have obtained it from their father, and that those who have inherited cDE must have done so from their mother. In the third generation it will be seen that we can be sure of the origin of the Rh genes in III.2, III.3, III.4 and III.5, and that of these only III.4 has elliptocytosis.

III.3 (CDe/cDE) is not elliptocytotic because she received CDe from her father and cDE from her mother. For the fourth generation we do not know the full Rh genotype of the husband of III.4 (he is not shown in the pedigree), but we do know that he was probably heterozygous CDe as IV.2 has this genotype and yet is not affected. IV.2 therefore probably received cde from her mother and CDe from her father. The elliptocytotic man IV.1 will have received his elliptocytotic gene from his mother with her CDe. The only alternative explanation for IV.2 being unaffected would be if there had been a cross-over in the gametes of III.4 between the births of her two children, whereby the gene for elliptocytosis got off her CDe and on to her cde, in which case IV.2 received CDe from her mother and cde from her father.

It will be seen that there is plenty to think about when scrutinizing a pedigree for linkage and when the laborious task of collecting the family data is finished there is a great deal of computer work to do as well. So far in medicine the use of linkages has been limited, but as more are found it will become increasingly important since it enables 'at risk' members of a family to be identified. Nevertheless, at the present time the study provides an intellectual fascination which gives some people a lifetime's work.

Association 7

7.1 Duodenal ulcer. Clinical features

The duodenum (so called because its length is about the width of 12 fingers) is the first part of the small intestine; it adjoins the stomach from which it is separated by the pyloric sphincter and is continuous with the next part of the small gut, the jejunum. Ulceration, which simply means loss of continuity of the mucous membrane, usually occurs in the first part of the duodenum, for it is here that the acid-pepsin mixture from the stomach impinges, whereas in the second part of the duodenum the contents become alkaline. Duodenal ulcer (DU) is but one example of 'peptic' ulcer, this being liable to occur at any site where acid comes into contact with the mucous membrane of the gut, e.g. in the stomach itself, at the lower end of the oesophagus when the sphincter is lax, and in a congenital sac (Meckel's diverticulum) which sometimes persists in the small bowel and contains acid-secreting cells. Plates 6 and 7 show X-ray pictures of a normal and an ulcerated duodenum after a barium meal; in Plate 7 the ulcer has penetrated into the deeper layers of the duodenum which therefore shows much scarring and deformity. The principal symptom of DU is pain two hours after meals, usually relieved by more food; occasionally there is bleeding into the gut, and sometimes perforation into the peritoneal cavity which leads to agonizing pain and board-like rigidity of the muscles of the abdominal wall.

7.2 Factors predisposing to duodenal ulcer. Association with blood group O

Once a DU has developed it is quite certain that factors such as increased gastric acidity, smoking and anxiety may make the condition worse, but no one knows why an ulcer arises in the first place, since it is normal for the acid contents of the stomach to come in contact with the first part of the duodenum, many people smoke, and everyone from time to time has anxiety. Inheritance probably plays a part, patients with duodenal ulcer tending to have children who develop the same condition, but no simple method of inheritance is responsible. Support for a genetic predisposition is that there is a striking association with blood group O, particularly in those cases where the ulcer has bled, and the main purpose of this section is to show how the validity of such an association may be tested.

7.3 Testing for an association between two characters

The association between blood group O and duodenal ulcer was established by collecting large numbers of patients with the disease and of normal controls, by the investigation of the ABO blood groups in both these groups and by the finding that there was a statistically significant excess of blood group O in the ulcer patients. Normally the controls consisted of healthy blood donors, students and nurses, but sometimes patients with diseases other than duodenal ulcer were used, though these are less satisfactory as there is always a possibility that the other diseases may be exerting some effect which has not been allowed for. The ulcer and control groups were then compared by means of the χ^2 test* and the value of χ^2 was highly significant. For Liverpool the χ^2 found when patients and controls of O and not O were compared was 44·26 with a probability of $< 10^{-10}$, i.e. the findings were enormously unlikely to have occurred by chance. An investigation of this sort often entails the consideration of whether it is legitimate to pool data from various localities, and it is not permissible to do this if the samples are heterogeneous, i.e. if the proportions of the characters being considered are significantly different from one another in the various samples which we want to pool. The χ^2 test for heterogeneity is worked out in exactly the same way as that for an association and if the value of χ^2 obtained is significant, it means that the figures in the various samples are heterogeneous and must not be pooled, but if it is not significant they can be. In the DU work all the data proved to be homogeneous and therefore poolable and the association was thus shown to be very highly significant.

7.4   Pitfalls in the selection of controls

While these results look conclusive, it is imperative to bear in mind a particular pitfall in the selection of controls, namely *racial stratification*. By this we mean that there is incomplete mixing of populations from different sources. An example is that among African Negroes a particular Rhesus blood group complex, known as cDe (see page 23), is very common, though it is rare among Caucasians. In a mixed population it would be highly unlikely that there would be random mating between Negroes and Caucasians and therefore there would appear to be an association between dark skin colour and cDe. This is an extreme example, but less well-defined degrees of stratification are common. For instance, in this country there are Jewish communities who tend to marry among themselves, and clearly if an association were found between dark complexion and diabetes (a disease which is very common in Jews) this would be of racial and not genetical origin.

7.5   Method of testing for an association using sibs of patients as controls

While *a priori* racial stratification seems unlikely to explain the association between group O and duodenal ulcer, it *might* be operating, and to

* See Bailey (1959) for the method.

eliminate any possibility that it was doing so our team in Liverpool used, at the suggestion of Professor L. S. Penrose, the unaffected brothers and sisters (sibs) of the patients as the controls; and the details of the method are as follows:

(i) The sibships must segregate (i.e. separate) both for blood group and for ulcer/not ulcer.

(ii) The chance of the propositus being group O is calculated in each sibship separately. Suppose there are four sibs in one family, two of group O and two of not O (e.g. A). One of these has an ulcer. Now the chance here of the ulcer patient being group O is clearly 50 per cent, i.e. 0·5, and so 0·5 is the 'expected' value in this sibship. We now look up the records, and if we find that he is in fact group O we enter the figure for that sibship as 1. If, on the other hand, he is group A we enter the figure for that sibship as O (zero). It will be seen that this method takes into account the fact that sibships are composed of different proportions of groups O and not-O; for example, in a family consisting of 6 group O and one group A sibs the chance of the propositus being group O would be much greater than it would be in one consisting of 6 group A and one group O sibs.

When all the families have been assessed we have therefore a total 'expected' and a total 'observed' score and we have to work out whether there is a statistically significant difference between them. This is done as follows and entails finding the variance in each family:

(a) Divide the number of group O individuals in the family by the total number of individuals in the family. This will give the 'expected' number of ulcer cases of group O.

(b) Multiply this value by the number of sibs who are not group O divided by the total number of individuals in the family. This will give the variance of the 'expected' value.

In our example of the sibship of four in which two sibs are group O and two are group A it will be remembered that the chance of the propositus being O is ½, and we can calculate that the variance is ¼ (see Bailey 1959).

(c) Now take the sum of the 'observed' values and the sum of the 'expected' values, and find the difference.

(d) next take the sum of all the variances and find the square root of it. This will be the standard error of the difference between the 'observed' and 'expected'—the 'observed' being, of course, the patients who actually are group O and the 'expected' being those who would be expected to be group O.

(e) Finally divide the difference between the 'observed' and the 'expected' by the standard error of the difference, that is, divide the value found in (c) by the value found in (d). *To be statistically significant the difference between the 'observed' and the 'expected' must be more than twice the standard error.*

To our surprise, after collecting about 160 segregating sibships, although we did find an excess of group O propositi observed over those expected, the difference was not statistically significant, but when combined with poolable data from the U.S.A. it became so, and the Establishment view now is that the association is a valid one (see Clarke *et al*, 1956.)

7.6 Association found to be due to a transfusion effect

Another pitfall which we discovered in Liverpool concerned an alleged association between duodenal ulcer and the Rhesus blood groups, but the association was found to be due to a *transfusion effect*, and this we think is so interesting that it will be described in detail. If individuals are simply scored as Rh positive and Rh negative no association is found between the Rh type and duodenal ulcer. However, it must be remembered that there are several different ways of being Rh positive because the Rh blood group is determined not by one gene but by *three* closely linked genes; each individual inherits two sets of these (derived from the two parents) and each set is inherited as a unit. For our purposes each unit consists of a combination of the well-known C, D, E, c, d and e antigens, all of which can be identified by the appropriate antisera, except for d, the antiserum for which has not yet been found (it is assumed that any individual who does not possess D is homozygous dd). It will be realized that as everyone inherits two units, they receive a combination of two from each of the C/c, D/d and E/e antigens.

Certain Rh positive combinations are commoner than others and we are accustomed to seeing particularly the following:

CDe/cde, or R_1r (34·9 per cent);
cDE/cde, or R_2r (14·1 per cent);
CDe/cDE, or R_1R_2 (13·4 per cent).

As regards the Rh negative combinations only those people who have two sets of cde are strictly Rh negative (rr) but in hospital practice, where the blood would normally only be tested with anti-D, individuals with a genotype such as cdE/cde, or Cde/cde would also be classed as Rh negative.

BUCKWALTER and TWEED (1962) *genotyping* their patients (i.e. not just testing for the presence or absence of the D antigen) found a highly significant association between the Rh positive combination CDe/cDE (R_1R_2) and duodenal ulcer and also blood type MN and this disease (in the MN blood group system the heterozygote MN can be detected serologically).

It occurred to our senior laboratory technician Mr. W. T. A. Donohoe that *transfusion* might be the cause of the association since he had observed (in common with many other people who actually *do* the work) that, using the five routine Rh antisera, there were sometimes produced, after a trans-

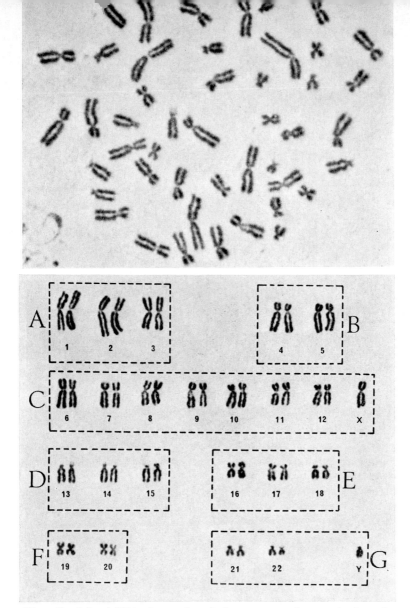

Plate 8 (*above*) This shows the 46 chromosomes from a single male cell undergoing mitosis. The chromosomes have doubled but are still held together by their centromeres. (By courtesy of Dr. S. Walker, Cytogenetics Unit, Nuffield Wing, School of Medicine, University of Liverpool.)

Plate 9 (*below*) This shows the same 46 doubled chromosomes as in Plate 8. The chromosomes are arranged in decreasing order of size and numbered from 1 to 22. The X and the Y are not numbered. The letters A to G show the various groupings; individual chromosomes in any of the groups may be difficult to distinguish from each other. (By courtesy of Dr. S. Walker, Cytogenetics Unit, Nuffield Wing, School of Medicine, University of Liverpool, and Messrs. Blackwell.)

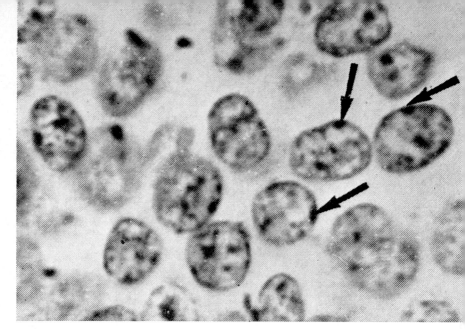

Plate 10 (*above*) Epithelial cells from the buccal mucosa of a female patient showing Barr bodies in the nuclei (chromatin positive). (By courtesy of Dr. Winston Evans, David Lewis Northern Hospital, Liverpool, and Messrs. Blackwell.)

Plate 11 (*below*) Foetal cells in the maternal circulation. The adult haemoglobin has been washed out of the mother's red blood cells and these therefore appear as 'ghosts'. The foetal haemoglobin is not eluted by the buffer and the cells therefore stain darkly. This method of detecting foetal cells is known as the Kleihauer-Betke technique. (By courtesy of Messrs. Blackwell.)

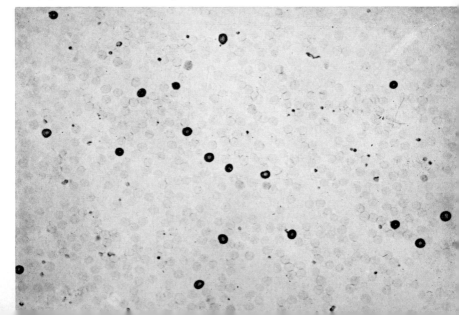

fusion, mixed cell agglutinations, indicating that the transfused cells contained antigens which the recipient lacked, these showing up as islets of agglutinated cells. An individual will of course be scored as positive for a particular antigen even if only a proportion of the cells is agglutinated by the appropriate antibody.

From a consideration of the frequencies of the various Rh genotypes in the population it was clear that the combination R_1R_2 was just the one which would be increased if transfusion were the cause of the association

Table 3 Blood groups before and after transfusion of the amount of blood stated

Case No.	Patient Pre-transfusion	Donor blood	Patient Post-transfusion
1	CDe/CDe MM	cDE/cde NN cDe/cde MN 2 pints (1140 ml.) of blood given	CDe/cDE MN Has gained c, E, and N antigens
2	CDe/cde NN	cDE/cde MM 1 pint (570 ml.) of blood given	CDe/cDE MN Has gained E and M antigens
3	cDE/cde MN	CDe/CDe MM CDe/cde MM 2 pints (1140 ml.) of blood given	CDe/cDE MN Has gained C antigen
4	cDE/cde MM	CDe/cDE NN cDE/cde MN cDE/cde MN CDe/cde MN 4 pints (2275 ml.) of blood given	CDe/cDE MN Has gained C and N antigens
5	CDe/cde MN	CDe/CDe MM cDE/cde MN cDE/cde MN 3 pints (1700 ml.) of blood given	CDe/cDE MN Has gained E antigen
6	cDE/cde NN	CDe/cde MM CDe/cDE MN 2 pints (1140 ml.) of blood given	CDe/cDE MN Has gained C and M antigens

CLARKE *et al.* (1962), by courtesy of the editor of *The British Medical Journal.*

4—H.G.M.

with duodenal ulcer. Similarly with the MN blood groups the frequency
of MN would be increased by transfusion.

Examination of Table 3 should make the matter clear, and the reader
should pay particular attention to the last column where he will see what
the patient gained in the way of antigens following the transfusion. It is of
interest that such gains persist often for a month following transfusion.

We clinched the matter by testing duodenal ulcer patients who were in
hospital (in either medical or surgical wards) and here we found the R_1R_2
association described by BUCKWALTER and TWEED—but over half of the
patients had been transfused. By contrast in a series collected as out-
patients who had had no recent transfusion the distribution of CDe/cDE
did not differ significantly from that of the general population. A similar
situation was found with respect to the MN groups (CLARKE et al. 1962).

Perhaps, when faced with an obscure association, as with an obscure
diagnosis, one should increasingly think of the possibility—has treatment
anything to do with it?

7.7   Cancer of the oesophagus and tylosis

We discovered in Liverpool two remarkable families in approximately
half of whose members there was a skin condition (tylosis) which is
characterized by thickening of the skin of the palms and soles. Tylosis is
inherited as an autosomal dominant character. The point about the tylosis

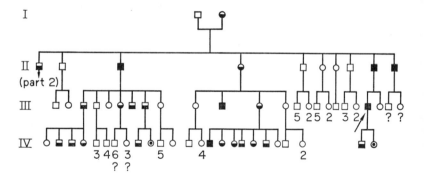

Fig. 7-1   Pedigree of cancer of the oesophagus and tylosis. (By courtesy of
Messrs Blackwell.)

in these families was that those with the skin condition are extremely likely to develop a cancer of the lower end of the oesophagus (gullet) and in no instance has any member who is non-tylotic developed the cancer. Figure 7–1 shows part of one of these families.

Common sense suggests that in these particular families the gene for tylosis also causes the stratified epithelium of the oesophagus to undergo a malignant change—in other words, the gene here has a pleiotropic effect which results in an 'association'. However, it is alternatively possible that we are dealing with two linked genes, one for tylosis and the other for the carcinoma, and that they are so closely linked that no crossing-over has occurred. This cannot be proved or disproved on our present knowledge, but if other similar families were found where the genes were in repulsion some members would have the cancer and some the tylosis. That is, the association would have disappeared and the evidence would strongly favour the existence of linkage.

Chromosomes

8.1 General

The somatic cells, no matter from which organ they are examined, contain 22 pairs of autosomes and two sex chromosomes, X and Y in the male and X and X in the female. It is now possible to examine and count chromosomes but they can only be seen in actively dividing cells and therefore the bone marrow is often looked at or cultures made from the lymphocytes in the peripheral blood or from skin. Whichever type of tissue is used the chromosomes appear as is shown in Plate 8 and it must be appreciated that what we are looking at is chromosomes in mitosis *not* meiosis.

In Plate 9 is shown how by convention the 22 pairs of autosomes are arranged and numbered in decreasing order and size. The X and Y are not numbered.

8.2 The Barr body

Examination of the chromosomes takes time and where abnormalities of the sex chromosomes are suspected useful preliminary information can often be obtained by looking at a stained preparation of cells from the inside of the patient's mouth. In the normal female can be seen a small darkly staining body under the nuclear membrane which is not present in males. It is known as the Barr body (see Plate 10) and this means that there are two X chromosomes in the nucleus because only one X chromosome is active in any one cell and it is the inactive one which stains darkly (see Lyon hypothesis in glossary). In males, because there is only one X chromosome in each cell, this is always active and there is no Barr body. People who have one or more Barr bodies are known as 'chromatin positive' and those who have none as 'chromatin negative'. It is not normal to have more than one Barr body, or to have none at all, if you are a woman. If you are a man, it is not normal to have one.

8.3 Three common medical conditions associated with chromosome defects

The three disorders to be described all have karyotypes which are abnormal in number, in one there being an abnormal number of autosomes and in two, an abnormal number of sex chromosomes. On occasion, however, two of the conditions may also be produced by structural defects.

8.3.1 *Down's syndrome (mongolism), caused by the presence of an extra small autosome*

This is named after LANGDON-DOWN, who first described the condition in 1866 and though it is still more commonly known as mongolism owing to the slanting eyes and slightly flattened face of the patients, this is for obvious reasons of international courtesy not such a suitable name. (In any event, it is of interest to note that the Mongoloid races think the patients have a European appearance and the resemblance to the Oriental is at most superficial; in fact it is quite easy to recognize Down's syndrome in patients of Oriental racial origin.) As well as the curious facial configuration and the narrow eyes, the patients are very short and there is mental retardation which varies from mild to severe, but the children have a happy and affectionate disposition. In newborn babies the condition can be recognized by the facts that the head tends to be small and oval, the ears low-set and with small lobes and the eyes slanting upward and outward; the bridge of the nose is usually absent or poorly developed and the mouth tends to hang open with the tongue out. Grey-white specks are seen in the iris of the eye (Brushfield's spots) and the little fingers are often short and incurved; the hands are broad and there are abnormal finger and palm print patterns. The life expectancy used to be about eight years, the children dying from infections, from heart defects and being more than usually liable to leukaemia. However, nowadays with the introduction of antibiotics and heart surgery they live much longer. Table 4 shows the frequencies of the syndrome at various maternal ages (and also the outlook for subsequent children) and it will be seen that the older mothers are much more at risk than the younger ones. The age of the father does not seem to be a factor.

Table 4   Relationship of maternal age to trisomy 21

Maternal age	Risk of occurrence	Risk of recurrence
20–30	1:1500	1:500
30–35	1:750	1:250
35–40	1:600	1:200
40–45	1:300	1:100
45-up	1:60	1:20

Redding and Hirschorn, 1968, by courtesy of the authors and the editor of the March of Dimes Original Article Series, Vol IV no. 4.

The usual type of Down's syndrome is caused by non-disjunction of the small chromosome pair 21. The mongol is trisomic for this and has a complement therefore of 47 instead of 46 chromosomes, and the technical name for the condition is trisomy 21.

Trisomies are produced by several types of error in cell division. The most common is known as meiotic non-disjunction, which means that a pair of chromosomes has failed to separate during the production of sperm or egg cells. This results in one cell containing both members of a particular pair of chromosomes and one containing neither. If the one with the extra chromosome joins with a normal cell (ovum or sperm) at fertilization, the resulting child will have three of that chromosome instead of a pair, and will be said to be trisomic for that chromosome (he will have 47 in all). If on the other hand the cell which lacks a chromosome unites with a normal cell, the resulting individual will be monosomic for that chromosome (and will have 45 in all). Monosomy as regards the autosomes is usually, if not always, lethal.

8.3.2 *Down's syndrome caused by translocation*

Less frequently, Down's syndrome is caused by a translocation (see glossary) between a number 15 and a number 21 chromosome. Figure 8–1

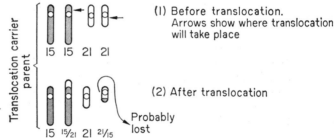

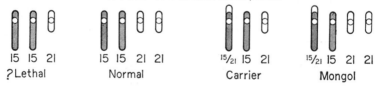

Fig. 8–1 Translocation in a mongol family. (By courtesy of Messrs Blackwell.)

demonstrates the method of inheritance of this type of mongolism. There is fusion of part of a chromosome 21 and part of a chromosome 15, but an individual carrying this abnormality will not be affected, because, even though he has an abnormal chromosome in the sense that he has parts of two stuck together, he still has no excess of chromosomal material. Those of his children, however, who receive his abnormal chromosome and *also* receive his normal 21 will be trisomic, because they will have received a normal chromosome 21 from their other parent.

This type of mongolism occurs in children of younger mothers, and it will be appreciated that it is not dependent on a chromosomal accident due in part to maternal age, but is brought about by the direct inheritance of an abnormal chromosome. Wherever there is a family history of mongolism in relatives, or where a young mother has already given birth to a mongol and is likely to have more children, it is well worth examining her chromosomes and those of her husband, and it would be very much the duty of a doctor to have such an investigation carried out. If a translocation is found in one of the parents, it will be seen from Figure 8–1 that there is an even chance of the child inheriting the translocation. If it inherits *both* the translocation *and* a chromosome 21 from its carrier parent, it will be a mongol because it has extra chromatin, the other 21 being derived from the normal parent.

8.3.3 *Mosaicism in Down's syndrome*

Sometimes non-disjunction occurs after the zygote has been formed. It is then mitotic in origin and errors can occur at any division, so that two or more cell lines may be established, and it is this which is known as chromosomal mosaicism (see Fig. 8–2). Mosaicism in Down's syndrome is of particular interest to the doctor since not infrequently one sees individuals who, though perfectly normal mentally, have some of the other

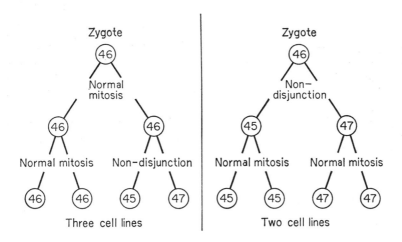

Fig. 8–2 The production of chromosome mosaics by mitotic non-disjunction after formation of a normal zygote. From *Chromosomes in Medicine*, Ed. Hamerton, 1962. (By courtesy of Dr D. G. Harnden and Messrs Heinemann Ltd.)

physical stigmata of the disorder, i.e. abnormal palm print patterns. The severity of the symptoms of Down's syndrome is directly related to the proportion of trisomic cells in the mosaic individual. The possibility that parents who have had more than one 'regular' (i.e. trisomic) mongol may themselves be mosaics must be considered. Such parents might appear normal or near normal but they could produce some normal and some 21 trisomic gametes, thus greatly increasing the risks to their children.

8.3.4. *Other (rare) chromosomal abnormalities involving the autosomes*

Trisomy of the 14–15 and 16–18 groups of chromosomes has also been described and this again produces mental defect. A deletion of part of chromosome number 5 is responsible for the cri du chat syndrome referred to in another connection (see page 7). In a particular type of leukaemia there is a very small chromosome 21 because of a deletion and this is known as the Philadelphia chromosome after its place of discovery. The exact relationship of the abnormality to the disease is not yet known.

8.3.5   *Klinefelter's syndrome (XXY), caused by the presence of an extra X chromosome in a male*

These patients look and behave like males, and it is highly probable that a proportion of cases go through life without ever consulting a physician, but they are completely infertile as even though erections can be obtained and ejaculations occur, spermatozoa are never present and the fluid is derived from the prostate and accessory glands. Some patients are married and consummation can be legally effected. The patients have small testes, are often tall and thin and have high-pitched voices. They may have abnormal development of the breast tissue and it is often only this which brings them to the doctor—particularly when it is noticed by other men as it used to be when National Service was in operation. In addition, there is a liability to mental defect, though many patients have normal intelligence.

The defect is caused by the fact that patients have an extra X chromosome, due to non-disjunction having occurred in one of the parents. They have therefore 47 chromosomes in all. Figures 8–3(a) and (b) show the results of non-disjunction of the sex chromosomes occurring (a) in a woman and (b) in a man.

These abnormal gametes are produced if the non-disjunction occurs at the *first* meiotic division. If it occurs at the second meiotic division as well, XX and YY sperm could also be produced, and four different types of abnormal offspring could result, XXY, XO and XXX as above, and also XYY. Males with this last sex chromosome constitution, XYY (produced by non-disjunction in a Y-bearing sperm) are often over six feet tall, tend to be extremely aggressive and *may* form a relatively high percentage of the inmates of institutions of the criminally insane.

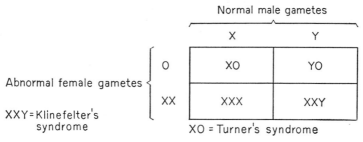

Fig. 8–3 (a)

These offspring, as can be seen, have an abnormal sexual constitution as follows:

XO   Abnormal female (Turner's syndrome) (see below)
YO   Almost certainly inviable (possibly because the X chromosome carries the gene controlling blood clotting factors)
XXX   Abnormal female (triple X). A rare condition but the patient is often surprisingly normal
XXY   Abnormal male (Klinefelter's syndrome)

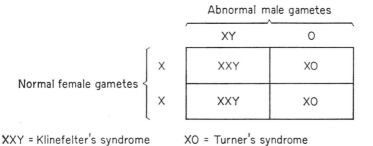

Fig. 8–3 (b)

Patients with Klinefelter's syndrome are chromatin positive (see page 46), that is they have a Barr body because they have two X chromosomes. It has been found by means of family studies, using the X-linked Xg blood group (see p. 12), that in Klinefelter's syndrome the non-disjunction has taken place in the father in about 40 per cent of cases and in the mother in about 60 per cent.

8.3.6   *Turner's syndrome (XO), caused by the lack of one of the two X chromosomes*

The characteristic picture of a patient with this condition is that of a very short girl having primary amenorrhoea (i.e. not having begun to menstruate) and who lacks the secondary sexual characteristics. There is often webbing of the neck (the skin filling in the angle of the neck and shoulders) and an increased carrying angle of the forearm, i.e. the forearm is 'set off' more than normal from the upper arm.

Most patients on skin sexing are chromatin negative (because the second X is lacking), and chromosome counts confirm that only 45 chromosomes are present, the missing one being an X and the condition arising because of non-disjunction (see Figs 8–3(a) and (b)). Family studies using the Xg X-linked blood group system have shown that the non-disjunction occurs more frequently in the father than in the mother in contradistinction to Klinefelter's syndrome (see above).

8.3.7 *Turner's syndrome caused by mosaicism, or by the formation of an isochromosome*

As with mongolism, however, the situation is not entirely clear-cut, and Turner mosaics, e.g. XO/XX, can occur and this explains why some of the cases (one-fifth of the total) are chromatin positive, i.e. have a Barr

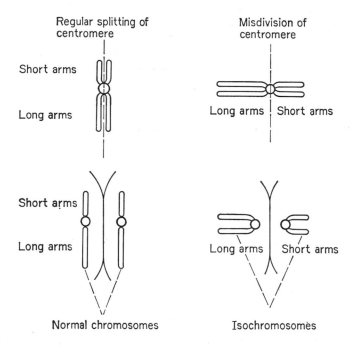

Fig. 8–4 The origin of an isochromosome through misdivision of the centromere during mitotic division.
(By courtesy of Dr. D. G. Harnden and Messrs. Heinemann Ltd., from *Chromosomes in Medicine*, Ed. J. L. Hamerton, 1962.)

body. Another reason is that the syndrome can also result from the single normal X being partnered by an abnormal X, that is an isochromosome, and Fig. 8–4 shows how this is formed. Sometimes the abnormal X is made up of two short arms and sometimes of two long ones, and although the individual has two XXs and therefore a Barr body, yet she lacks some of the genes which make her a normal female, i.e. those on the missing long or short arms. A consideration of many cases with both types of isochromosome suggests that genes present on the long and the short arm of *both* X chromosomes are necessary for the development of a functioning ovary, whereas genes apparently influential in the development of stature, and of the other somatic features which are frequently abnormal in Turner females are on the short arm, and that the short arms of *both* Xs are needed for normal somatic development (see *Br. Med. Bull.*, 1969).

Pharmacogenetics is defined as a study of genetically determined variations in animal species which are revealed by the effects of drugs. Three examples are given here.

9.1 Acatalasia. Clinical features

This is an extremely interesting disease originally described in Japanese families, affected individuals being liable to severe ulcers in the mouth. To understand the condition it is necessary to remember the following points:

(*a*) Hydrogen peroxide dropped on to a raw surface in a normal person froths and the blood does not alter in colour. This is because the peroxide is degraded by an enzyme in the tissues called catalase, and oxidation of haemoglobin by hydrogen peroxide is thereby prevented.

(*b*) In patients with acatalasia frothing does not occur and the tissues turn brown because haemoglobin *is* oxidized.

(*c*) Certain bacteria (particularly some known as haemolytic streptococci) themselves produce hydrogen peroxide, and in a patient lacking catalase the haemoglobin of the blood reaching any tiny abrasion in the mouth is oxidized so that death of the tissues occurs because the infected area is deprived of oxygen. In this situation the bacteria multiply, the hydrogen peroxide production increases and a vicious circle is established.

Only about half of those who lack the enzyme actually show symptoms and those who do usually exhibit their disability before the age of 10 years, the bones of the jaw becoming infected, this leading to the loosening and loss of teeth. However once all the teeth have been removed the ulcers heal and many patients remain permanently free of symptoms. A similar condition has also been found in certain breeds of dog and guinea-pig.

9.1.1 *Method of inheritance of acatalasia*

There is good evidence that the trait behaves as an autosomal recessive character. Consanguinity is frequent and not a single parent of an affected individual has had the condition. Catalase estimations on patients and their sibs give a trimodal distribution, the intermediate values being those of the presumed carriers of the trait.

More recently Swiss workers have found two examples of acatalasia on screening 18,459 blood samples from Army recruits and it is of interest that in neither case was there any clinical abnormality.

9.2 Primaquine sensitivity

Haemolytic anaemia, that is anaemia produced by the breakdown of red blood cells and not by haemorrhage, was recognized as an occasional complication of an antimalarial drug, pamaquine, when it was introduced into medicine in 1925. At first the anaemia was thought to be due to a hypersensitive or immune mechanism, but an antibody was not discovered and no explanation could be found for the occurrence of haemolytic anaemia in these sensitive subjects.

With the advent of widespread malaria treatment with the very similar drug primaquine during World War II more cases of a similar haemolytic anaemia were studied.

9.2.1 Clinical features of primaquine sensitivity

When a sensitive subject is given 30 mgm primaquine daily he does not develop haemolytic anaemia for two or three days. Thereafter his urine gradually turns dark, muscular pains occur and anaemia and possibly jaundice appear. Discontinuing the drug results in a return to normal over a few weeks. However, if the symptoms are not severe and primaquine ingestion is continued he will, surprisingly, also gradually improve. It will be seen later that this is a most important observation.

9.2.2 Labelling experiments

Light was thrown on the mechanism of the anaemia when Cr^{51}-labelled red cells were transfused from sensitive subjects into non-sensitive recipients. The survival of these cells was normal until primaquine was administered, when they became lysed. When Cr^{51}-labelled cells were transfused from a normal subject into a sensitive individual, they survived normally, even when primaquine was administered, and even when the patient's own red cells were lysed under the influence of the drug.

The fact that a sensitive subject gets better despite continued drug administration was investigated by similar methods. Thus, selected labelling of red cells of narrow age range with Fe^{59} resulted in the finding that red cells in a sensitive subject can be lysed by primaquine when 63 to 66 days old but not when 3 to 21 days old. Therefore, it seems that it is the ageing red blood cells which are destroyed by primaquine. Spontaneous clinical recovery while continuing with drug ingestion is due to the regeneration of a red cell population with a low mean age.

9.2.3 Biochemical studies

The normal red cell is known to possess enzyme systems which are concerned with the metabolism of glucose. One of these is glucose-6-phosphate dehydrogenase, *which is diminished in primaquine-sensitive individuals*. The first observation which led to this discovery concerns reduced glutathione. Thus, when both sensitive and non-sensitive red cells are incubated with primaquine *in vitro*, their content of reduced glutathione falls (Fig. 9–1), but this can be prevented *in normal individuals only* by adding glucose to the buffer in which the red cells are suspended. The reason for the continued fall in sensitive red cells is due to a fault in glucose metabolism, ultimately the result of a defect in glucose-6-phosphate

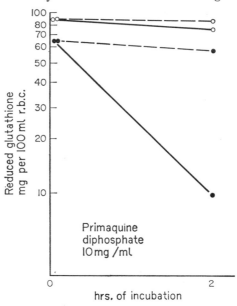

Fig. 9–1   The effect on reduced glutathione of incubating sensitive and non-sensitive red cells in the presence of glucose. (BEUTLER *et al.*, 1960, by kind permission of the McGraw-Hill Book Co. In *The Metabolic Basis of Inherited Disease*, Ed. Stanbury, Wyngaarden and Fredrickson.)

oxidation (dehydrogenation) due to a deficiency in the appropriate dehydrogenase (G6PD) and Fig. 9–2 explains the metabolic defect in relation to glutathione.

9.2.4 *Genetic studies*

Males are readily assignable to either the sensitive or non-sensitive group on both glutathione and G6PD studies. Women do not give quite so clear-cut a division and intermediate values are observed with either method of assessment.

Site of metabolic defect in primaquine sensitivity

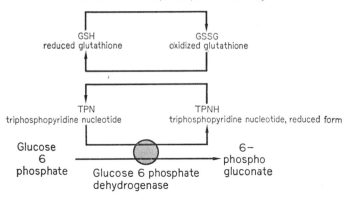

Fig. 9–2 The hydrogen atom removed from G6P by G6PD is taken up by TPN and TPNH is formed. This in turn reduced GSSG to GSH. If G6PD is deficient, the cycle is interrupted and no GSH is formed. (EVANS & CLARKE, 1961 by courtesy of the authors and the editor of the *Brit. med. Bull.* **17,** 234.)

On investigating 30 sibships it was found that male to male transmission was rare, appearing only once. The usual picture was that of an 'intermediate' female who produced sensitive sons or 'intermediate' daughters (cf. haemophilia, see page 8).

Pedigree analysis and the sex differences led to the conclusion that the gene controlling the presence or absence of G6PD is on the X chromosome, i.e. the trait is a sex-linked 'dominant', the penetrance of the gene being incomplete because 'intermediate' daughters and sensitive sons are sometimes found to have apparently normal parents. Colour vision studies also established that G6PD deficiency was sex-linked and investigations with the Xg^a antibody (see page 12) then showed that the gene was close to the Xg locus which itself is probably on the short arm of the X chromosome.

9.3   The metabolism of Isoniazid

9.3.1   *Family studies*

Isoniazid is a drug, discovered about 1952, which is extensively used in the treatment of pulmonary tuberculosis. It had been known for a long time that people were either 'good' or 'poor' excretors according to whether they excreted large or small amounts of the compound in the urine and this led to the suggestion that there were, in fact, two genetically controlled classes in the population, the 'rapids' and the 'slows' and a pair of autosomal genes were thought to be responsible, rapid inactivation being dominant to slow. However, in the early work there was a considerable overlap in the two classes so that the scoring of some individuals was doubtful. EVANS and his colleagues (1960) therefore carried out a much bigger investigation and used a more accurate method of assay. Taking 484 people they estimated the plasma concentration of isoniazid six hours after a single oral dose of 10 mgm per kg body weight, and found a bimodal distribution with an antimode at 2·5 µg/ml. Of the 484 individuals studied, 267 were members of 53 complete, two-generation, Caucasian family units, and Fig. 9–3 (see below) shows the isoniazid distribution histogram for these

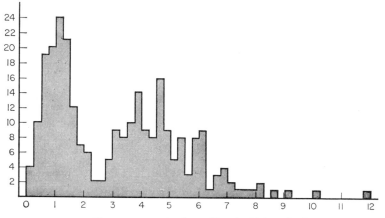

Plasma concentration of isoniazid (µg/ml)
6 hrs. following oral administration of 9·7 mg per kg of body weight

267 family members — 53 families

Fig. 9–3 Distribution of plasma isoniazid concentration. The rapid inactivators (R) are to the left of the antimode and the slows (S) to the right. (From EVANS *et al.*, 1960, by courtesy of the authors and the editor of *Brit. med. J.*)

subjects. It will be seen that approximately half were slow (S) and half rapid (R) inactivators, and analysis of the mating types confirmed that the slow inactivator character was indeed recessive (Table 5).

9.3.2   *Dosage effect*

Of great additional interest was the fact that a dosage effect was demonstrable. Thus the mean plasma isoniazid concentration of all rapid inactivators was found to be lower than that of a group of known heterozygotes. This is what would be expected if the homozygous rapids (who would be included under 'all rapid inactivators') had lower readings than the heterozygotes.

Table 5   Observed numbers of children of each phenotype compared with those expected on the hypothesis that slow inactivation of isoniazid is an autosomal recessive character. Remember that R can be heterozygous or homozygous.

Expected numbers of children of each phenotype compared with those observed

| | | | No. of children of each phenotype | | | | | |
| | | | R | | S | | | |
Pheno-typic matings	No. of matings	No. of children	expected	observed	expected	observed	χ^2	D.F.
S × S	17	54	nil	4	54	50	—	—
R × S	23	67	38·88	40	28·10	27	0·075	1
R × R	13	38	31·30	31	6·68	7	0·018	1
	53	159		75		84	0·093	2

$$P > 0.95$$

EVANS *et al.* 1960, by courtesy of the authors and the editor of the *Brit. med. J.*

9.3.3   *Medical implication*

The most important medical implication of this research is that slow inactivators are much more likely to develop neurological complications of the drug than are the 'rapids'.

9.3.4   *Anthropological aspects*

From the anthropological point of view it is of interest that the proportions of the two phenotypes in an Indian population closely resemble that in the Caucasian and the American Negro. On the other hand, there is a much larger proportion (> 90 per cent) of rapid inactivators in the Japanese, and Eskimo populations consist almost entirely of this phenotype. The advantage of the dominant character is not known but it would appear that its possession is particularly helpful in the Far Eastern and Arctic environments.

9.3.5   *Site of acetylation of isoniazid*

EVANS (1963) has shown conclusively by *in vitro* experiments that it is the rate of acetylation that distinguishes the two classes and that it is in the liver that this takes place. He used fresh biopsy specimens of human liver and after suitable preparation incubated them at 37°C with isoniazid. Two hours later the amount of free drug was estimated and from this the amount acetylated was calculated. The 'slow' and 'rapid' results obtained tallied with the inactivator status (carried out later) on the owners of the livers.

Prevention of Rhesus Haemolytic   10
Disease of the Newborn, Exemplifying
Genetics and Preventive Medicine

10.1 Clinical aspects of the disease

Babies whose blood is incompatible with that of their mother on the Rhesus blood group system (mother Rhesus negative, baby Rhesus positive) can suffer from very severe anaemia caused by the release of haemoglobin from the child's red cells owing to the action of antibodies formed by the mother. She may have made these antibodies because she has earlier had an incompatible blood transfusion, or because she has had a previous Rh incompatible baby and a few cells from the baby have leaked across into her circulation—usually at delivery. The maternal antibodies are rather slow to form, with the result that it is always (or very nearly always) a previous baby which has caused them. Affected babies can die *in utero*, or just after birth, but more often they survive and present with jaundice and liver failure and occasionally they are deaf or mentally retarded. Sometimes—in fact often—they can be rescued by a complete exchange of all their blood, and mildly affected babies recover on their own. It is, however, a very serious worry to couples where the wife is Rhesus negative and the husband Rhesus positive. About 85 per cent of the population of this country is Rhesus positive, so the chances of a Rhesus negative woman having a Rhesus positive husband are very high.

10.2 Risks of the baby being affected

The risk of the baby being affected is luckily *not* very high: among the 850,000 births each year in Britain, for instance, the number of 'Rhesus' babies is probably not more than about 5000. Several factors operate to limit the risk. First, leakage of the baby's blood through the placenta into the mother's circulation in sufficient quantity to stimulate the production of Rh antibodies does not occur often. Second, some women do not produce antibodies even if there is leakage. Third, when the Rh positive father is heterozygous (having received an Rh negative gene from one of his parents) there is only a 50 per cent chance that the baby will be Rh positive. Fourth, and this is what particularly interested us in Liverpool, in about 20 per cent of all the potential cases the formation of antibodies is prevented by the protective mechanism arising from interaction with the blood group genes of another system, namely the ABO.

10.2.1　*Protection by ABO incompatibility between mother and foetus*

This operates particularly when the blood of the Rh negative mother is group O, because group O blood always contains naturally-occurring antibodies against group A and group B blood. When, therefore, her baby is not group O, but is either A or B (it will never be AB because A and B are alleles and the baby can have received neither from his O mother) the mother's naturally-occurring anti-A or anti-B will destroy—or at any rate in some way get rid of—any baby's cells which have leaked across into her circulation (see Fig. 10–1). These cells have the Rhesus antigens on them

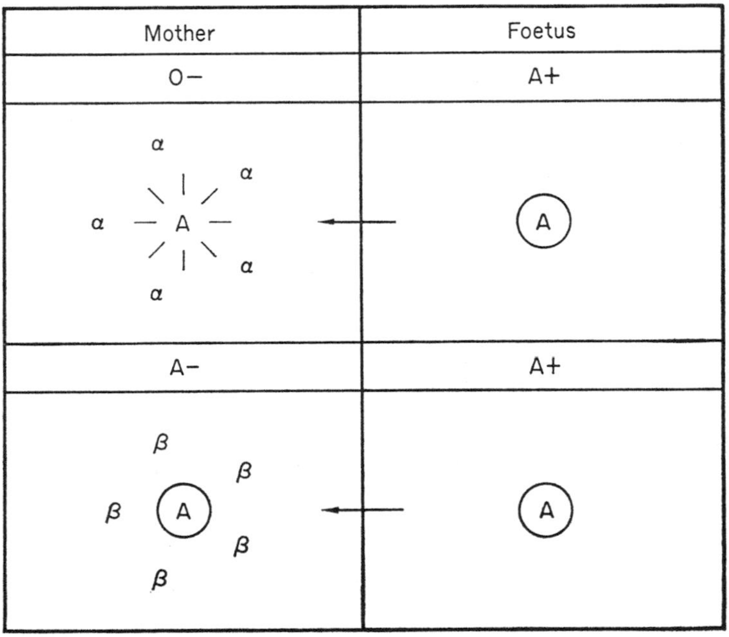

Mother	Foetus
O–	A+
	A
A–	A+
	A

Fig. 10–1　In the upper half of the Figure a red cell from a group A Rh positive foetus is crossing the placenta and is entering the circulation of a group O Rh negative mother where it will be immediately destroyed by the naturally occurring anti-A (α). Conversely, in the lower half, a red cell from a group A Rh positive foetus is entering the circulation of a group A Rh negative mother where it will survive normally, its life span being many weeks. (By courtesy of Messrs Blackwell.)

of course, as well as the A or B antigen, and therefore this Rhesus antigen will have been rendered harmless *before* the mother has time to make the anti-Rhesus antibody (it will be remembered that the antibody is quite slow to form). It will be realized that while some antibodies are naturally occurring others are 'immune', that is they are formed in response to an antigen and are not present in the normal way. Nobody makes Rhesus antibodies unless they are *caused* to make them.

10.3   Mimicking the natural protection by ABO incompatibility by giving anti-Rhesus antibody

We tried to think of a way by which we could mimic this natural type of protection by ABO incompatibility in women who were not protected by it, and it seemed that there was a very distinct possibility that if we gave the mother anti-Rhesus antibody (anti-D is the most important type) immediately after the baby's birth we might be able to destroy any Rhesus positive cells in the mother's circulation before they had time to do any harm.

10.4   Experiments on male volunteers

We decided to test out the hypothesis on Rh negative men and in the first experiments we took a group of male volunteers and injected into them Rh positive adult red blood cells labelled with radioactive chromium. Half of the volunteers were kept as controls and the other half were given the anti-Rh antibody about half an hour after the original injection.

The results were exciting—the injected anti-Rh did indeed get rid of a high proportion of the Rh positive cells. However, to our dismay we found that six months later, instead of preventing the men from forming antibodies, actually *more* men had formed them than would have been expected by chance—we had enhanced instead of suppressing antibody formation. However, we felt that our reasoning was basically sound, and very fortunately we did not let ourselves be discouraged. We tried a different kind of antibody and found that we had given the wrong type the first time. We had given the 'complete' form of antibody, which acts in saline solution, and this we found had left the residue of the cells still antigenic even though the cells themselves had gone. We therefore did a second set of experiments using 'incomplete' anti-Rh, which 'coats' the antigen so that it cannot make contact with the antibody-forming cells. These were much more successful and prevented antibody formation in almost all the subjects treated.

10.5   Experiments with foetal blood in women volunteers

We next found that this same procedure was successful when *foetal* (instead of adult) red cells were used, and when the subjects were Rh negative *women* volunteers who were past the child-bearing age.

10.6   Relation of the formation of Rhesus antibodies to the size of the foeto-maternal bleed

We also established by means of a survey among Rh negative women that the likelihood of their forming antibodies against their Rh positive children generally depended directly on the *number* of foetal cells which had crossed the placenta, and these could be recognized by a special staining technique (see Plate 11).

10.7   The Liverpool clinical trial

We felt, therefore, that the time was ripe for trying the treatment on primiparae* who had had an Rh positive, ABO compatible baby and had had a considerable transplacental haemorrhage since these women would be the ones most seriously at risk. The importance of the choice of this 'high risk' group should be clearly realized—it is not necessary to know much in the way of statistics to appreciate that if we treated these women (and kept similar women as controls) we should know much sooner whether the treatment was successful or not than if we treated women who were less at risk. The experiment was carefully planned to give an answer *quickly*, before many women had been subjected to a procedure which might be of no use and might even have unforeseen disadvantages or dangers.

We therefore took from five Liverpool maternity hospitals all Rh negative women who had had a Rhesus-positive, ABO compatible baby and who had had a 'big' bleed, i.e. 5 cells or more of foetal blood per 50 low power fields of the microscope, and we treated *alternate* ones, the others being kept as controls. The treatment consisted in giving 5 ml (about 1000 μg) of anti-Rh, in the form of gammaglobulin, to the mother within 36 hours of delivery, and we tested to see if the foetal cells were in fact diminished during the next few days, and later to see if by the time six months had gone by—when the mother might have begun to make antibodies and the injected antibody would almost certainly always have disappeared—whether the mother had made anti-Rhesus antibodies. The results were astonishingly successful; practically no treated mothers made antibody and many controls did; it was far better than we had hoped; in all biological procedures there is variation and error and we should have been perfectly satisfied if we had protected 75 per cent of cases. In fact we protect far more—about 95 per cent—and now with a smaller dose (about 200 μg). The treatment is being carried out in many parts of the world and in general controls are no longer being used. Currently much of the experimental work is concerned with the size of dose, since it is necessary to know how much gammaglobulin is effective for the bigger bleeds (where most of the failures lie) and also what is the smallest dose which will protect the vast majority of women.

---

* i.e., women delivered of their first baby.

10.8   Results in subsequent pregnancies

The real test of the success or failure of the treatment lies in the results of subsequent Rh positive pregnancies. Unbelievers told us that the anti-Rh gammaglobulin was only 'holding down' the immune antibody formation and as soon as the woman had another baby overt antibody would be found. This does not appear to be so since hundreds of women from the various centres have had subsequent babies—some several—and there are very few failures. So genetically determined diseases are not necessarily hopeless from the point of view of prevention. (See CLARKE 1968 and CLARKE 1969 for summaries of the work and for references.)

11.1 General. Advice in terms of odds

With the spread of medical knowledge there is an increasing desire among the public to read the future and the commonest request is for information about risks to subsequent children when one has already been born with an abnormality. Alternatively, parents knowing of a skeleton in the family cupboard, may ask about the chances of its turning up in their grandchildren—though not infrequently what they really want is medical backing against a union of their children they dislike on other grounds. Least commonly of all, individuals about to get married may seek advice about risks to offspring, but couples who do this are often obsessional—

Table 6   Empiric risks for some common disorders (in per cent)

Condition	Normal parents having an affected child	Normal parents having a second affected child	Affected parent having an affected child
Congenital dislocation of the hip	0·07 (1M:6F)	5	5 (but see p. 14)
Hypertrophic pyloric stenosis	0·3 (5M:1F)	4	6
Harelip with or without cleft palate	0·1 (2M:1F)	4	4
Cleft palate only	0·04	2	7
Epilepsy	0·5	10	5
Clubfoot	0·1 (2M:1F)	5	7
Anencephaly	0·2 (1M:3F)	5	—
Spina bifida	0·3		
Hydrocephalus	0·2		
Schizophrenia	1·0	14	16
Mental retardation (non-specific types)	1·0	15	35

EMERY (1968). By courtesy of the author and Messrs. E. and S. Livingstone.

most young people who have decided to get married pay no attention to what a doctor says, and in general this is probably a healthy type of reaction.

Advice on genetic matters should always be given in terms of probability, never certainty, and in these days of football pools patients readily understand odds. A helpful though somewhat frightening yardstick is that about one pregnancy in 30 will produce either a marked congenital malformation or a serious developmental abnormality which appears early in life: e.g. harelip, spina bifida, congenital heart disease, mental deficiency (see below and Table 6) (FRASER ROBERTS, 1970).

11.2 Situations where fairly precise information can be given

Fairly precise information can only be given in the minority of cases, i.e. those which show clear-cut Mendelian inheritance, and even this may necessitate the study of many pedigrees. When it is found, the risks to subsequent offspring are too high to be acceptable to most people. Some examples follow:

(*a*) In a disorder controlled by an autosomal dominant gene (e.g. Huntington's chorea (see page 2) the chance of any given offspring having the disease if one parent be affected is one in two, and the risk is similar for subsequent siblings—chance has no memory.

(*b*) If a child is born with a recessive trait (e.g. fibrocystic disease, see page 3) the risk of subsequent offspring being affected is one in four. The same is true of phenylketonuria, which results in mental deficiency because of the lack of the enzyme phenylalanine hydroxylase which normally converts phenylalanine into tyrosine. This disorder, however, requires further comment. With treatment (the low phenylalanine diet) patients may survive and affected girls marry. In most cases their spouses will be normal men and therefore their children, though heterozygous, would all be expected to be phenotypically normal. However, it has recently been shown that phenylalanine from the affected mother (who often relaxes the strictness of her diet in pregnancy) can cross the placental barrier and render *all* the children mentally defective, though they are not, strictly speaking, phenylketonurics.

(*c*) If the disease is due to an X-linked recessive gene (e.g. haemophilia, see page 8), then an affected male married to a normal woman will have all carrier daughters but all his sons will be unaffected. Of the daughters of a carrier female half will be normal and half carriers and of her sons half will be affected and half normal. This is well known, but in a disease such as haemophilia, if there is no family history it is very important not to give the rather bad prognosis for relatives until one has considered the possibility of a mutation (see page 10). If this has occurred in the patient then none of his sisters would be carriers. It may be very difficult to decide the point but enquiries about the disease in maternal uncles and great-uncles is important.

(*d*) In the translocation causing mongolism there is about a one in four chance that a child of a carrier will be a mongol (see page 48).

11.3 Situations where the risk is empirical

In contradistinction to the above it often appears from the family history, particularly in common conditions, that there is a genetic component to the illness but this is not transmitted in any clear-cut way. This may be for various reasons:

(*a*) the disorder may be determined by many genes (multifactorial inheritance as in high blood pressure, see page 14),

(*b*) the environment may be also partly responsible,

(*c*) there may be heterogeneity with differing factors responsible in the various sub-groups of the disease.

In such situations the risks are empirical, the definition of this term being 'the probability of occurrence of a specified event based upon prior experience and observation rather than on prediction by a general theory' (HERNDON, 1962).

Table 6 gives the empirical risk figures for some of these conditions.

11.4 Notes on some of the disorders mentioned in Table 6

(*a*) Congenital dislocation of the hip

Here infants are born with the disorder which varies from a minor radiological change in the acetabulum (the socket in the pelvis for the hip bone) to a severely incapacitating lesion. Several factors have to be taken into account. Two of these are genetic, one affecting the development of the acetabulum (probably multifactorially controlled) and the other producing an increased laxity of all joints (a dominant trait). There is also an environmental component, namely the intrauterine posture.

(*b*) Hypertrophic pyloric stenosis (see also p. 14)

Here there is pathological hypertrophy of the sphincter between the stomach and the jejunum. The condition occurs in infants (particularly boys) and leads to intractable vomiting because of the obstruction. A simple operation whereby the hypertrophied muscle fibres are slit usually gives good results. An interesting observation is that affected children subsequently have exceptionally well-developed musculature.

(*c*) Anencephaly, spina bifida and hydrocephalus

These are abnormalities of the central nervous system and together account for a large proportion of all congenital deformities. In anencephaly a part of the skull and brain fail to develop and the condition is incompatible with survival. Hydrocephalus, which may be associated with spina bifida, results from obstruction to the flow of cerebrospinal fluid around the brain and the head is consequently large. In spina bifida there is a defect in the vertebral column through which part of the spinal cord and its coverings may protrude, though sometimes the condition is trivial.

11.5 Detection of carriers

Another important aspect of genetic advice is the detection of carriers in recessive conditions. As far as the autosomes are concerned there are only two (fibrocystic disease and thalassaemia), which are of importance since, in general, recessive diseases are extremely rare. In cystic fibrosis of the pancreas (see page 3) (frequency about 1 in 2000 live births) skin fibroblast cultures show cytoplasmic metachromasia (see page 5) not only in the affected children but also in their parents who are obligatory heterozygotes (DANES and BEARN, 1968). Thalassaemia, with a frequency as high as 5 to 15 per cent in some parts of Northern Italy and in Thailand, is a disease characterized by anaemia and it results from an abnormal gene which controls the rate of production of normal haemoglobin so that in many cases the red blood cells of the adult contain only foetal haemoglobin. Patients with two doses of the gene usually die young from gross anaemia but those who are heterozygotes may be mildly affected or not at all. It is important to detect these carriers and this can be done as a screening procedure, by estimating the fragility of the red blood cells which are unusually resistant to haemolysis by hypotonic saline solutions, i.e. they do not blow up and burst as easily as normal red blood cells.

The detection of the carrier state is of much more importance in the commoner X-linked conditions (for example in advising the sister of a man with haemophilia) and in general the assessments are made by biochemical methods. For example, in haemophilia there is a relative lack of one of the clotting factors (factor VIII) in the female carriers, so that it is now possible to detect these women in about 85 per cent of cases. Again, in an X-linked muscle disorder (muscular dystrophy) it is possible to recognize the female carriers in about 70 per cent of cases by estimating one of the muscle enzymes (serum creatine kinase) which is increased compared with normal women.

There is much more to counselling than what has been written here and readers are referred to EMERY (1968). As he says, 'Medical genetics seems likely to become the preventive medicine of the future.'

Glossary

Allelomorph (allele)   One of two or more contrasted genetic characters.

Antibody   A protein produced in an animal when a certain kind of substance (an antigen, q.v.) which is normally foreign to its tissues gains access to them.

Antigen   Substance capable of stimulating the formation of an antibody (q.v.).

Autosome   Any chromosome other than the sex chromosomes (X and Y).

Barr body   Small darkly staining body under the nuclear membrane of mammalian somatic cells present in normal females but absent in normal males (see p. 46).

Cistron   (see p. 23)

Crossing-over (syn. recombination)   The exchange of genes between homo-
.logous chromosomes which takes place at meiosis.

Deletion   Loss of part of a chromosome.

Dizygotic twins   These result from the fertilization of two separate eggs at the same time and two such twins are no more genetically similar than sibs. Another type of twin could be produced if two halves of an ovum were fertilized by two different spermatozoa. If this happened the twins would have an identical set of genes from the mother but a different set from the father.

Dominance   A character is said to be dominant if the gene controlling it produces the same effect in the heterozygous as in the homozygous state.

Drift   (see *genetic drift*).

Expressivity   The degree to which the effect of a gene is expressed. If the gene is controlling a disease some of those inheriting it will be more severely affected than others—e.g. in neurofibromatosis some individuals will have skin tumours, pigmentation and bone changes, whereas others will have pigmentation only.

Fitness (syn. biological fitness)   The fitness of an individual is measured by the number of his or her offspring who reach reproductive age. An individual is said to have unit fitness if he or she has two such offspring (not one, as each child must have two parents).

Genetic drift   The establishment of certain gene frequencies in small populations—not owing to natural selection but owing to the original genetic constitution of the ancestors of the population, or chance survival when a population is reduced.

Genotype   The genetic make-up of an individual with regard to a given pair of alleles—a blood group A individual may be of genotype AA or AO. (c.f. phenotype, q.v.)

Hardy-Weinberg rule   Unless disturbed by outside influences, e.g. natural selection, the proportion of the various genotypes in the population remains the same in each successive generation provided that the particular genes carried by an individual do not influence the choice of mate—i.e. mating is random.

Heterosis   Hybrid vigour.

Heterozygous   Possessing two different allelomorphs at the two corresponding loci on a pair of chromosomes.

Homologous chromosomes   Chromosomes which are homologous pair with each other at meiosis and contain identical sets of loci (q.v.).

Homozygous   Possessing similar allelomorphs at the two corresponding loci on a pair of chromosomes.

Inversion (chromosomal)   Because of aberrant cross-overs within chromosomes a segment can become inverted and the genes will then appear in the wrong order.

Karyotype   The artificial arrangement of the chromosome set so as to allow comparison of their morphology and subsequent analysis. Chromosome pairs range from 1–22 together with the sex chromosomes XX or XY (Denver classification). They are more readily recognized in groups (Patau classification) which correspond to the Denver system as follows: Group A (1–3), B (4–5), C (6–12), D (13–15), E (16–18), F (19–20) and G (21–22).

Linkage   Genes situated on the same chromosome are said to be linked. Except when crossing-over (q.v.) occurs they are inherited together. Crossing-over occurs less frequently the nearer together the genes are situated.

Locus   The site on a chromosome occupied by a particular gene, or by a member of a particular allelomorphic series.

Lyon hypothesis   According to the Lyon hypothesis one of the X chromosomes in every female somatic cell is inactive, and it is this X chromosome which constitutes the Barr body (q.v.).

Monosomy   Where one chromosome of an homologous pair is missing. Hence the individual only has 45 chromosomes.

Monozygotic twins   These result from the division into two of the embryo derived from a single fertilized ovum and such twins are genetically identical.

Mosaic   An individual with cell lines, or tissues, of different chromosome numbers or constitutions.

Multifactorial inheritance   (see p. 14).

Mutation Change in a gene (see p. 10).

Non-disjunction The failure of two homologous chromosomes to pass into separate gametes either at meiosis or mitosis.

Penetrance A dominant gene is said to have full penetrance when the character it controls is always evident in an individual possessing the gene. A gene controlling a recessive character is said to be fully penetrant if the character is invariably manifest when the genes are present in double dose.

Penetrance = frequency with which any effect is shown in a population.

Expressivity = degree to which effects are shown in an individual.

Phenotype The manifest genetic make-up of an individual, e.g. the information available from the examination of a single individual, without reference to any family (breeding) data. (c.f. genotype, q.v.)

Pleiotropy Multiple effects of the same gene. A gene might have a major effect such as that controlling the production of a blood group antigen and also play a minor part in predisposing to duodenal ulcer, for instance.

Polymorphism The occurrence within a freely interbreeding species of widely differing inherited forms, the rarest of them being too common to be kept in existence by recurrent mutation.

Propositus The individual through whom the investigation of a pedigree is begun; usually but not always an 'affected' individual.

Recessive A character is said to be recessive if it is only manifested in those homozygous for the gene controlling it. It is not detectable (except sometimes by special tests) in the heterozygote.

Recombination (see *crossing-over*).

Sex-linkage A gene is said to be sex-linked when it is on part of either the X or the Y chromosome. If it is situated on the non-pairing part of the Y it can never cross over on to the X and will therefore always be handed from father to son. If a gene is on the X a man will pass it on to all his daughters and a woman to either son or daughter.

Spock test Spock and his colleagues found that affected individuals and carriers of fibrocystic disease possess an abnormal globulin which interferes with the normal rhythm of the cilia on the respiratory tract tissue of rabbits.

Super-gene Term used to denote a series of genes which have become closely linked on the same chromosome owing to the selective advantage of their being inherited as a unit.

Trisomy Where one chromosome is represented by three homologues as opposed to the normal two. Hence the individual has 47 chromosomes.

Translocation This happens when two pieces of chromosome (not of the same size) are broken off from two non-homologous chromosomes and their positions exchanged (reciprocal translocation). The result is then that one chromosome will have too little chromatin and the other too much.

Xg blood group   A blood group system which is sex-linked, i.e. the genes controlling the characters are on the X chromosome. In the original series tested 61·7 per cent of men were Xg(a+) while 38·3 per cent were Xg(a−). For women the percentages were Xg(a+) 88·8 and Xg(a−) 11·2. The reason for the difference between the male and female percentages is that some of the Xg(a+) women are heterozygous. (RACE, R. R. and SANGER, R. 1962, *Blood Groups in Man*, 4th Ed. Oxford.)

Zygote   The fertilized egg.

References

ALLISON, A. C. (1954). 'Protection afforded by the sickle-cell trait against subtertian malarial infection'. *Br. med. J.*, i, 290–294.

BUCKWALTER, J. A. and TWEED, G. V. (1962). 'The Rhesus and MN blood groups and disease'. *J. am. med. Ass.*, **179**, 479–485.

CLARKE, C. A., EDWARDS, J. WYN, HADDOCK, D. R. W., HOWEL EVANS, A. W., MCCONNELL, R. B. and SHEPPARD, P. M. (1956). 'ABO blood groups and secretor character in duodenal ulcer. Population and sibship studies'. *Br. med. J.*, ii, 725–731.

CLARKE, C. A., DONOHOE, W. T. A., MCCONNELL, R. B., MARTINDALE, J. H. and SHEPPARD, P. M. (1962). 'Blood groups and disease: previous transfusion as a potential source of error in blood typing'. *Br. med. J.*, i, 1734–6.

CLARKE, C. A. (1968). 'Prevention of Rhesus iso-immunisation'. *Lancet*, ii, 1–7.

CLARKE, C. A. (1969). 'Prevention of Rhesus iso-immunisation'. *Seminars in Haematology*, **6**, No. 2, 201–24.

DANES, B. S. and BEARN, A. G. (1968). 'A genetic cell marker in cystic fibrosis'. *Lancet*, i, 1061–1063.

DANKS, D. M., ALLAN, J. and ANDERSON, C. M. (1965). 'A genetic study of fibrocystic disease of the pancreas'. *Ann. hum. Genet.*, **28**, 323–356.

EVANS, D. A. P., MANLEY, H. K. and MCKUSICK, V. A. (1960). 'Genetic control of isoniazid metabolism in Man', *Br. med. J.*, ii, 485–91.

FISHER, R. A. (1930). *The Genetical Theory of Natural Selection*, Oxford.

FORD, E. B. (1940). *The New Systematics*, Ed. HUXLEY, J., Oxford.

HAMILTON, M., PICKERING, G. W., FRASER ROBERTS, J. A. and SOWRY, G. S. C. (1954). 'The aetiology of essential hypertension'. *Clin. Sci.*, **13**, 11–37 and 265–73.

HERNDON, C. N. (1962). 'Empiric risks': In *Methodology in Human Genetics*, Ed. W. J. BURDETTE, Holden-Day, San Francisco.

LAWLER, SYLVIA D. and SANDLER, M. (1954). 'Data on linkage in Man: elliptocytosis and blood groups, IV—families 5, 6 and 7'. *Ann. Eugen. (Camb.)*, **18**, 328–334.

MIALL, W. E. and OLDHAM, P. D. (1958). 'Factors influencing arterial blood pressure in the general population'. *Clin. Sci.*, **17**, 409–44.

PENROSE, L. S. (1959). 'Natural selection in Man: some basic problems'. In *Natural Selection in Human Populations*. Pergamon Press, London.

PICKERING, G. W. (1959). 'The nature of essential hypertension'. *Lancet*, ii, 1027–8.

PLATT, R., (1959). 'The nature of essential hypertension', *Lancet*, i, 55–7.

PLATT, R. (1963). 'Heredity in hypertension'. *Lancet*, i, 899–904.

PRICE, J. (1967). 'Human polymorphism'. *J. med. Genet.*, **4**, 44–67.

RENWICK, J. H. (1963.) 'Male and female recombination in Man'. Paper read at the XIth International Congress of Genetics, the Hague.

RENWICK, J. H. and LAWLER, SYLVIA, D. (1955). 'Genetical linkage between the ABO blood group and nail-patella loci'. *Ann. Eugen. (Camb.)*, **19**, 312–319.

SHEPPARD, P. M. (1958). *Natural Selection and Heredity*, Hutchinson, London.

SPOCK, A., HEICK, H. M. C., CRESS, H. and LOGAN, W. S. (1967). *Pediatr. Res.*, **I**, 173.

VOGEL, F. and CHAKRAVARTTI (1966). 'ABO blood groups and smallpox in a rural population of west Bengal and Bihar (India)'. *Humangenetik*, **3**, 166–80.

Bibliography

BAILEY, N. T. J. (1959). *Statistical Methods in Biology*. English Universities Press, London.

British Medical Bulletin. Human Genetics. British Council (1969).

CARTER, C. O. (1962). *Human Heredity*. Penguin, Harmondsworth.

CARTER, C. O. (1969). *An ABC of Medical Genetics*, The Lancet, Ltd., London.

CLARKE, C. A. (1964). *Genetics for the Clinician*, 2nd. ed. Blackwell, Oxford.

CLARKE, C. A. (ed.) (1969). *Selected Topics in Medical Genetics*. Oxford University Press, London.

CLARKE, G. M. (1969). *Statistics and Experimental Design*. Edward Arnold, London.

EMERY, A. E. H. (1968). *Elements of Medical Genetics*. Livingstone, Edinburgh.

FORD, E. B. (1956). *Genetics for Medical Students, 4th ed*. Methuen, London.

FORD, E. B. (1965). *Genetic Polymorphism*. All Souls Studies. Faber and Faber, London.

MCKUSICK, V. A. (1969). *Human Genetics, 2nd. ed*. Prentice Hall.

PENROSE, L. S. (1963). *Outline of Human Genetics, 2nd. ed*. Heinemann, London.

ROBERTS, J. A. FRASER (1970). *An Introduction to Medical Genetics, 5th. ed*. Oxford University Press, London.

STERN, CURT (1960). *Principles of Human Genetics*. Freeman, San Francisco.

Studies in Biology

sponsored by The Institute of Biology

St. Martin's Press, Inc., New York